CRAFT

POEMS

*Printed and published in Great
Britain by D.C. Thomson & Co.
Ltd., 185 Fleet Street, London
EC4A 2HS. © D.C. Thomson & Co.
Ltd., 2006.*

ISBN

D0240576

Curtain Of Pride

by Isobel Stewart

*With each other they didn't have
to hide the pain of past — all the
 re reason to be honest
in the
"He ut the future ...*

I N the end, it was over so quickly. Lynn sat huddled at the gas fire, her hands around a mug of coffee that had cooled without her knowing it, while Steve packed. His clothes, his books, his CDs.

It was her flat; the furniture and the pictures were hers, the curtains and ornaments. All things she had wanted, had saved for, but all of them cold and comfortless when he had gone.

"I've met someone else," he had said, only putting words to what she had feared, what she had been more and more certain of.

Sometimes she thought she had known from the first time she saw them together, at his firm's Christmas party.

He had gone to get her a glass of wine, and she had watched him cross the crowded room, stopping to speak to a fair-haired girl, laughing at something she said.

"Julie, who sorts out our computer problems," he'd said a little later, when he introduced them. "And this is Daniel, her fiancé."

They'd talked for a while, the four of them, then someone had called Julie's name, and she and Daniel moved away.

There weren't, in fact, so many times when she saw them together, Lynn realised later. The office sports day, one or two Saturdays when Steve had to pick something up from the office and Julie was there, a cinema queue once, a wine bar another time.

Chance meetings, she would tell herself, but with each one Lynn's foreboding grew. Until the day Steve's words confirmed all her fears.

And after that it was over so quickly and she was alone, alone with the memories and the broken dreams.

Her friends did their best.

"You're better off without him."

"You'll meet someone else."

"Just as well you weren't married."

Lynn wondered about that sometimes. Would it have made any difference if they had been married?

She didn't know, and in any case it didn't really matter. She knew her friends were trying to help her, and so she nodded and agreed with them, until she felt that her whole body ached with the effort of pretending her entire world hadn't fallen apart.

Because they didn't understand, any of them, how she really felt and there was no way she could make them.

Perhaps that was why everything changed on the night she met Daniel.

Daniel, Julie's fiancé. She hadn't given him more than a passing thought, she realised, ashamed, when they both stopped in the crowded railway station.

Ashamed, because she could see in the shadows under his eyes, the thinness of his face, how bad it was for him, too.

"Lo, Lynn," Daniel said quietly.

Around them, the busy home-bent people hurried and swirled.

"How have you been?" he asked her.

And the words died on her lips, the bright, positive, untruthful words she had forced herself to keep on saying.

"Not good," she said a little unsteadily, but honestly. "And you?"

"Not good either," he replied. "In fact, pretty lousy."

He tried to smile. "Are you in a hurry?"

Lynn thought of the bleak loneliness of the flat she had once been so thrilled with and shook her head wordlessly.

"Let's go and have something to eat," he said.

LYNN couldn't quite remember, afterwards, what they'd had to eat in the little coffee bar round the corner from the station, but it didn't matter. Nothing mattered except that this man understood.

He understood how she felt, he understood her loss, he understood her attempts to hide behind an oh-so-thin curtain of pride.

He understood, because he was right there, too.

"Did you know?" she asked him. "Before Julie told you?"

"I think I knew from the first time I saw them together," Daniel said slowly, and she knew he had thought about this as many times as she had. "I couldn't put my finger on it, but — there was something."

"I thought so, too," Lynn agreed. She could see once again the two of them, Steve and Julie, standing in a crowded room, Julie's fair head thrown back as they laughed together.

"And each time after that, I was more and more sure."

She looked at him across the table. "Did you ever ask her?"

"Never," he said. "I kept thinking if I didn't put it into words, the whole thing might —" He hesitated.

"Might just go away?" Lynn suggested.

Daniel smiled, and for the first time his smile almost reached his eyes.

"No-one else understands that," he said quietly.

Lynn remembered the diamond ring on Julie's left hand.

"Were you planning to get married soon?" she asked him.

His grey eyes clouded and he drew a deep breath.

"She wanted a Christmas wedding," he said at last. "So that's what we were planning." He was silent for a moment then asked, "What about you?"

"Steve never talked about marriage, and neither did I. But if he had asked me, I would have married him."

"It helps, talking to you," he said. "Other people don't understand."

"I know," she agreed.

LYNN met Daniel again by arrangement a few nights later, and they went on to a film. They both enjoyed themselves, laughing at the same bits. Afterwards they went for coffee.

"It's good finding that someone else is on the same wavelength, isn't it?" Lynn said.

And as she said it, she stopped, realising the significance of that remark and knowing that he'd realised it, too.

"Yes," Daniel said, his voice low. "I suppose they do laugh at the same things, Julie and Steve."

She looked at him. "What do you think they found in each other, that they didn't find in us?" she asked him not quite steadily.

He shook his head. "I don't know," he said at last.

Then he leaned across the table, and covered her hand with his.

"Come on," he said, "I'd say we're not that bad, you know, for a pair of rejects!"

And it wasn't as difficult as she had thought it would be to smile . . .

He didn't move his hand from hers for some time, and that night when they parted, he kissed her, his lips warm on hers, his arms holding her close to him.

They got into the habit of seeing each other every second night, and then of meeting occasionally at lunchtimes. And then, gradually, Daniel started coming to her flat, where she would cook him a meal, and they would watch an old film on television.

And bit by bit, as the weeks went by, she heard about how he and Julie had met at a friend's wedding, how they had both known right away how they felt about each other.

The dreams they had had, the plans they had made.

"Do you know, we had even chosen names for the children we were going to have?" Daniel said one night. "Simon and Laura, they were going to be. And we didn't really mind which came first, we said."

Lynn looked down at her clasped hands. Steve had never put a ring on her left hand, never talked about the children they might have.

She wondered if he and Julie talked about having children, if they'd chosen names.

"We had dreams, too," she said, her voice low. "Different dreams. Back-packing in America. Working in a ski lodge in Austria."

But the dreams were gone now, she thought, gone with Steve.

Daniel's hand covered hers.

"Hey, I bet it isn't all beer and skittles for them — Julie has a real Irish temper."

"And Steve is the world's most untidy and unpunctual man," Lynn returned.

She would have liked to add — and good luck to them. But she didn't feel like wishing them good luck, and she was pretty sure neither did Daniel.

"I don't know how I would have come through this without you, Lynn," he said once. In fact, if it hadn't been for Daniel, Lynn didn't know how she would have coped with the nauseating wave of emptiness that washed over her when she read, in the paper a few weeks later, that Steve and Julie were married . . .

QUIETLY, the notice said," she told Daniel. It was hard to keep the bitterness out of her voice.

"That was decent of them, wasn't it?" he said bleakly.

It was only now that each of them finally had to accept that it was over.

Perhaps it was this realisation that marked the beginning of a change in their relationship, Lynn thought afterwards. Nothing dramatic, just something different in the way he kissed her, the way he held her.

And somehow, without anything being said, there grew to be a sense of a shared future.

Most of the time, Lynn was happy about this.

Daniel has helped me, and I've helped him, she thought.

Of course, it isn't the same kind of relationship as before, she told herself, for me or for him. But that doesn't make what we have any less good. It's just different, that's all.

Because she had come to know Daniel so well, to feel so close to him, she realised, a few weeks before her birthday, that he was thinking of giving her an engagement ring.

Sometimes when she thought of this she could see herself with the ring on her left hand.

But there were other times, times when she found herself wondering.

Not worrying, she would tell herself hastily. Just — wondering . . .

★★★★

"Are you coming home for your birthday, Lynn?" her mother asked one evening on the phone.

Lynn hesitated. "I don't think so, Mum," she said at last, carefully.

There was a small silence. She had been home only twice in the months since Steve left and she was sure this was the weekend Daniel hoped to propose.

The thought awoke a confusing swirl of emotions in her.

"Tell you what, Mum, I will come home this weekend," she said.

She knew Daniel would be disappointed that she was going away and hadn't asked him to go with her . . .

IT was good being home, Lynn decided. Her parents, her brother, the old dog, the neighbours — the dear familiarity of it all surrounded her like a warm blanket.

On Sunday morning, when her father and her brother were playing golf, and Lynn and her mother were in the kitchen together, peeling vegetables, her mother said comfortably, "He's done you a lot of good, your Daniel. You want to bring him with you next time."

And suddenly Lynn knew that she had to tell her mother the truth.

"Mum," she said slowly, "Daniel is the man Julie was engaged to."

"Oh!" Her mother was taken aback.

Lynn told her, then, of how she and Daniel had met, how much they had been able to help each other, how well they got on together.

"Yes, I can see it's helped you over this bad time," her mother said very carefully. "But I get the feeling that there's something bothering you, something you're not completely happy about."

"This isn't a rebound thing, Mum," Lynn said not quite steadily. "Daniel and I didn't meet right away."

Her mother sighed. "I don't mean to interfere, I just want you to be sure."

I am sure. Lynn thought.

She opened her mouth to say the words, to reassure her mother. But didn't say them.

"We share so much, Daniel and I," she said instead.

SLOWLY, over the two-hour train journey back, Lynn's formless doubts began to take shape, and she knew she wasn't sure.

It was, above all, the past, the shared feelings of betrayal and loss, that held Daniel and her together.

She couldn't hide from her misgivings any longer. Right from the start, she and Daniel had been honest with each other, and she couldn't go back on that.

"We have to talk, Daniel," she said, as he held out his hand to help her down from the train.

He didn't say anything, only looked at her, and her resolution almost failed her.

I can't do it, she thought, to him or to myself.

But in the coffee bar — the same one they had gone to that first night all those months ago — she began to say, painfully, the things she had to say.

"We've helped each other so much, Daniel," she began. "We both know how much we've needed each other. But perhaps in a way what we're doing now isn't building a new life, but holding on to the old one.

"Perhaps what we each need now is to let go — let go and move on."

He smiled, and her heart ached, because the smile didn't reach his eyes, it was the kind of smile he had had when she met him first.

"You mean we're both carrying too much emotional baggage," he said bluntly.

"Yes . . ." Lynn answered honestly. "And maybe just being together makes it difficult to let go of that baggage."

"I prefer to think that we've helped each other to carry it."

"Of course we have," Lynn replied, not quite steadily. "Oh, Daniel, we have. But I think we each have to learn to stand alone now."

"Is that what you want?" he asked.

For a moment, a wave of panic swept over her. It would be so easy to say no, she had been foolish, they would just go on as they had been, and forget all that she had been saying.

But she knew that she couldn't do that. This was right for them both, right and necessary.

"Yes," she said, as steadily as she could. "It's what I want, Daniel."

"Maybe you just need time, maybe this is too soon for you," Daniel said. "I won't rush you, Lynn. I can wait."

"I do need time," she agreed. "And so do you. But — not together, Daniel."

She was completely certain of that now. She knew there would be times when she would miss him, his sympathy, his understanding. She knew that she would always be grateful for these months. But she knew, too, that she had to go on from here without him. And if it was wrong for her to go on depending on him, then it was wrong for him, too.

The rain had stopped, and a few uncertain stars were shining, and the moon had come out from behind a bank of clouds as they walked down the street.

"I'm not going to say goodbye, Lynn," he said with a sudden decision. "I think you may well be right, and we both need to learn to stand alone. But, perhaps at the end of that, if we were to meet again, we might find we were free of the past and it was just you and me after all."

Lynn shook her head. "I'm not making any promises, Daniel. It wouldn't be fair to either of us."

She waved down a passing taxi, and as it pulled up farther down the street, she turned to him to say goodbye.

He kissed her, warmly, briefly.

"I'm not saying goodbye," he said again. "Just au revoir."

"No promises," she said, not quite steadily. Determinedly she walked towards the waiting car and got in.

The taxi moved away, slowly at first but gathering speed. It wasn't easy, but she didn't look back . . . ■

Return To Smuggler's Cove

by Jill Painter

*She came here every year
to remember the past —
and look forward to the future...*

JANE SEWELL descended the rough stony path to Smuggler's Cove carefully. It was a path she had trodden since childhood and, because she knew of its treachery, had no intention of falling victim to it.

On the far side of the narrow inlet and at eye-level to where she stood, the wooden bench, newly-painted green in readiness for summer visitors, beckoned her as it always did.

The March wind tugged at her headscarf and, far below, the same gusts pushed the white-capped waves into thundering horses, making them gallop across the sand and crash against the cliffs.

Exhilarated, smiling, she tucked a wisp of silver hair back under her scarf and looked at the bench. That was her goal.

Every March she made her way to the wind-blown spot as an act of love, a kind of annual pilgrimage to the past.

The beauty spot had no regular place in her life as it was today, yet it was still an important part of her life.

It was the part she considered to be the beginning . . . the start of it all . . .

★★★★

The war was already two years old. The beautiful coastline protected by barbed wire; at night a vast dark area lit only by the vicious flash of incendiary bombs.

Pretty dresses and cream cakes were no more than a memory. Despite this, Jane's days seemed filled with endless sunshine — and all because of David.

That wild March day she sat on the bench and waited. She saw him in the distance.

Not for him the easy way; not down the stony path which was long and tedious. Oh no, he took the short cut, leaping down the tussocked hill like a young gazelle.

Tenderly, she watched him, hardly able to wait until he reached her side. When he did, his breath clouded warmly into the cold, crisp air and his face shone with pleasure.

He wasn't in uniform. There was no Navy blue; no brass buttons. Instead he wore shapeless grey trousers and a thick white sweater which accentuated his tanned face and his startlingly blue eyes.

"I'm late," he said breathlessly. "Sorry." Then he sat beside her, stretching his legs out and letting his head fall back.

"What happened?" she asked, not really caring just as long as he was here.

"I ran out of time." He smiled boyishly, shamefaced. "I had a report to do and I'd forgotten it."

"Never mind," Jane smiled, "You're here now."

"What shall we do? Walk across the headland, maybe?"

For some reason she didn't want to. There would be too much space for her mood. She needed to feel enclosed, sheltered.

"I wish we could get on to the beach," she sighed. "There are some marvellous rock pools down there at Smuggler's Cove."

They were a childhood memory. Bright, shimmering, never-to-be-forgotten images.

David pulled her to her feet, his touch making her heart leap and her hands tremble.

"Then to Smuggler's Cove we will go!" he laughed.

"But, David," she half protested, "it's all barbed wire — and it's a restricted area. And there are great poles all over the place."

"We'll find a way," he laughed. And she laughed with him, suddenly so happy, just because he had said "we" not "I". It made all the difference . . .

The rock pools were limpid and surprisingly warm.

"Did you ever see such colours?" she cried, watching his reflection in the still water.

A crab scuttled and a sea-anemone, prettily fronded, withdrew into a plum-coloured blob. The crab, mindful of its soft shell, disappeared into a narrow cleft, glad of the safety.

"What a life," Jane said, with vague longing for such tranquillity. "So secure, a little pool, a little house —"

"And a great big tide to swamp it all!" David shouted suddenly, dragging her towards the cliff face.

The tide had turned and the waves, foam-topped, crashed and spattered about them. Stabbingly cold, it tasted salty and smelled of seaweed.

They raced for the sandy bay, slipping and sliding on the smooth, damp rocks.

She fell and lay there laughing, breathless, seeing him silhouetted as a dark shadow against the blue sky.

Suddenly her laughter died. The heady joy vanished and in that timeless and infinitesimal moment she became afraid.

He pulled her to her feet and held her close. They stood together as the roaring, incoming tide sparkled and crashed into the once-quiet pools.

It was then she realised that the words she longed to hear, the words she knew David wanted to say, didn't have to be voiced. She knew, and he knew, they were unnecessary.

They stood together in the quiet knowledge that that was where they belonged.

Yet she was still afraid.

AT the top of the cliff, she sat on the bench, fingering the old, weathered, gnarled wood, while David stood beside her, hands in pockets, gazing out across the ocean.

There was something about his stillness, his stance, that sharpened her fears.

"Davey?" She used his pet-name only when she was troubled.

He turned and smiled and his beautiful blue eyes were clouded by unhappy thoughts. "I have to go away," he told her.

"For ever?" she asked, dreading his reply.

"Don't be daft!" He smiled, then looked serious again. "No, not for ever — but for a while."

"Where?"

"You know I can't tell you that . . ."

"When?"

That he could tell her — but the knowledge chilled her.

"So soon!" she cried out in shock. "I thought everyone was given embarkation leave!"

He held her cold hand with warm, entwined fingers.

Later, she wondered why hadn't he told her that this was his embarkation leave. There was no excuse except that he hadn't wanted to mar their time together.

"Look!" He broke the silence. "There's a seal!"

Her eyes, tear-filled, followed the point of his finger to the inquisitive creature, bobbing on the waves.

"Isn't he a beauty!" David cried. She longed to agree, to catch and share his wonder, but she saw no beauty . . . only loneliness.

The sun went behind a white cloud and the seal disappeared.

David put his arm about her and drew her close.

"I'll miss you, Jane. I'll miss these moments, and I'll miss the magic of this spot. But it will be only for a little while. I'll be back! And when I am we can begin again."

She gazed into his eyes, loving him to the point of pain.

"Yes," she said. "We will begin again. Your leaving will be no more than — than turning a page in a book."

"A book we know!" He smiled, gently.

"A story with a happy ending?" And her voice was confident.

"Of course!"

With that, she knew it had all been said. They belonged to each other. For now. For ever.

And so David went away, leaving a void which no amount of letters could fill.

Spring merged into summer. Autumn drifted into winter.

The war developed with intensity, yet, in all the madness of the world, the wooden bench at the top of the cliff was Jane's haven.

To sit there and look out to sea created a fragile bond with David to which she clung.

WHEN he came home on his first leave, he was a changed man. There was a steeliness about him, a toughness that was etched in his face.

The smile was the same — if less ready — but his blue eyes were clouded with the horrors he had seen. Not that he spoke of them. He told her only of the cold and tiredness.

"It's too cold to sleep, Jane. And you'd never believe the thickness of the ice on the ship's superstructure."

She shivered despite the warmth of his embrace.

"It sounds dreadful."

"It's a man's world."

"No pretty W.R.N.S.?" she teased, needing to see him smile.

"Only ugly gulls!" he quipped and the laughter which followed was shared.

How sweet that leave was — how warm and tender. And how strong she chose to be.

She would not let him dwell on anything beyond their own world of rock pools on a forbidden beach, an old wooden bench and their love.

When he returned to his ship, the lines on his face were not quite so deeply etched and with that Jane had to be content.

On his second leave, they had their first serious quarrel. David did not want her to go to the bench any more.

"Why not?" she asked with surprise.

"Because it's too exposed, too dangerous. All it needs is a trigger-happy Hun flying over and you wouldn't stand a chance."

"That's nonsense!" she protested. "Who's going to shoot a solitary girl when there's an aerodrome not a mile away, and a village even less. He'd more than likely go there if he wanted to take pot shots!"

"Pot shots! Now you're being childish," he accused her angrily.

"Think what you like! The war's not going to rule my life!"

"Why not?" he asked bitterly. "It rules mine!"

Stunned by the truth of his words, she was immediately contrite. Even so, she could not promise not to return to the bench.

After that there were no more leaves for David, for the next time Jane saw him he was home for good, but walking only with the aid of two sticks. Tessy and Bessy he called them. But he bore no grudge.

In time his blue eyes danced again. Yet sometimes, when she secretly watched him, she knew he longed to take the stony path to the bench, to climb the tussocked hill. Sadly, it was not to be. The war had been very thorough.

THEIR wedding was simple. A gown of white. A bouquet of spring flowers and then home to their stone cottage. David learned watch repairing and their life ticked by to a regular beat.

March was the only time of disquiet. The only time when they seemed to be at odds with the world, but that, too, finally fell into the rhythm they longed for.

It was David who asked her to go to the sea at Smuggler's Cove alone.

"But why, Davey?" she asked unsurely.

"Because it belongs to us in March," he told her simply.

Now she travelled the path alone, rested on the bench and, because it was important to David, she searched for a grey seal. Sometimes she saw one. Sometimes she didn't. Other than that, little changed.

The spot held the same magic, the words spoken were clearly heard and dearly remembered. And always the silent vows echoed in her heart.

In the village beyond, in their grey stone cottage, filled with the scent of rosemary and thyme, David, too, would be remembering.

★★★★

Now, shivering slightly as the March wind came in from the east, she turned her face homeward; to warmth and familiarity.

David was in his chair, the cat purring on his knee, Tessy and Bessy to hand and the kettle singing on the hob.

"All right?" he asked, touching her cold hand.

"Perfect," she told him. "The wind was blustering and sharp, the sea a gallop of white horses and they've painted the seat green again. I even saw a seal!"

He nodded, smiling.

"Did you sleep at all?" she asked.

"Yes, and I dreamed," he told her, "of bright rock pools and scuttling crabs."

She kissed him gently and laid his hand on her cheek.

"I never did tell you, on that far away day, that I loved you," he said.

"You didn't have to."

"How did you know?"

"How did either of us know?"

He shook his white head in wonder.

"Shall we have scones for tea?" Jane asked.

"As we did on that March day all those years ago? Oh, Jane," he said contentedly, "we could write a book about our life, couldn't we?"

"The best ever." She smiled.

"With chapters yet to be written!"

"Many, many more," she promised.

The kettle sang, the cat purred and, in Smuggler's Cove below the green bench, a seal bobbed on the white-capped waves. ■

*A poem by Joyce Stranger, inspired by
an illustration by Mark Viney.*

A TREASURED PICTURE

*You sent me a picture
I will certainly treasure;
A scene in the country
Which always gives pleasure.
A world away from the crowded city
And overworked folk I can only pity.
Tumbled clouds in a soft blue sky
Birds on the lake and a dragonfly.
A solitary rabbit wiles away hours
Perched among reeds and wild growing flowers.
Growing trees reflections cast;
Above them a bird is flying past.
The heron wades, and is poised to strike,
Unaware that near him lurks a pike.
A thrush on a post . . . I can imagine his trills
As his glorious voice the silence fills.
I wish I was there with a view of the hills.
I draw the blind and hide the street.
Ignore the sounds of passing feet.
Hours of pleasure are mine to take
As I sit and look at the pictured lake.*

I didn't know whether I'd come to
Fernriver to say hello or goodbye —
I only knew that I needed
your blessing . . .

As Free As The Breeze

by
Della
Galton

HELLO, David. I don't say the words out loud. It's been a long time since I've needed to do that. Five years to be precise. I blink in the sunlight and stare out across the sloping green fields. It's just as beautiful as I remember it.

Wild grass sways gently, undulating as if there's all the time in the world, as if there's nothing to do except grow slowly upwards in perfect peace towards the milky blue sky.

You loved it here.

"Fernriver is Summer," you once told me, your blue eyes laughing into mine. "It's the air. It's so soft against your face," and you drew the tip of your index finger across my forehead and down the line of my cheekbone as if to demonstrate.

I know what you mean. I breathe the sweet Fernriver air deep into my lungs, feeling my head spin slightly. Then I walk down towards the stream.

There's a lesson to be learned from that stream, I think idly. Moving forwards, always forwards, crossing the obstacles in its path without trouble, without fuss.

"Marry me, Lisa." I can hear the words now, hear them in the whispering of the breeze through the grass. "Marry me, Lisa."

I walk a little way, following the winding stream, feeling my feet sink into the soft, earthy bank. There are pink and yellow flowers growing here, but I don't know what they are.

You would have known. You were good at things like that. The whole countryside was an open book that you could caption with ease.

Gipsywort, Water Mint, Flowering Rush, you knew them all. I wish I'd taken more notice, but I was content just to listen to you, letting your enthusiasm for the outdoor world wash over me.

I've reached a part of the stream now where it widens out, its shingle banks sloping upwards. We had a picnic here once.

I carried the blanket from the car and you brought a bag containing baguettes and soft cheese and apples.

We sipped red wine with our feast and we talked and laughed until the sun turned the sky a soft pink and dusk stole around us, bringing midges who had no sense of romance at all, but were intent on moving us on our way.

That was the night that you convinced me that the only way to avoid being bitten was to do something so crazy that no self-respecting midge would come near you! It involved standing in the stream and splashing a lot while singing loud tuneless songs.

We ended up collapsing with laughter and getting quite a bit wetter than I'm sure was necessary. It worked though, we didn't get bitten once!

There's a slight tightening in my throat and I realise with surprise that it's not tears, but laughter, that gathers there.

"Oh, David —" and this time I do speak out loud "— it's taken me all this time, all these anniversaries, to realise that it's OK to laugh."

It's odd, isn't it, how the happiest memories are the ones that cut the most deeply? As if there's somehow a price to pay for that joy, an equal and matching memory of pain.

I can't believe I'm laughing. The part of me that's still detached observes that I am probably hysterical. But I know that it's something deeper than that.

It's as if I can hear your voice deep in my mind, saying, "It's OK, Lisa. It's OK to remember with joy."

I STAND still for a moment and close my eyes, feeling the faint warmth of the sun on my hair. I remember a day like this long ago, when you lifted your face up to the sky and said, "humans are so strange, walling themselves up in concrete boxes. We should never be inside when there are places like this left on earth."

That was the very essence of you; a wild thing, a restless, dreaming romantic. I knew you'd never be caged by convention and sometimes I worried about you. But most times I was happy to be with you, sharing a closeness that I'd never known with another human being.

I N THE end, it wasn't me or convention that clipped your wings, but a dark shadow on your lungs, a blotch on an X-ray.

"You're still young, Lisa. You will have your life to live. You're too young to grieve forever."

There's no pressure in the words, only gentleness and understanding, yet . . .

I shake my head. When I was a child, I used to pretend I was a horse. I'd gallop around our garden, snorting and whinnying and driving Mum and Dad mad.

I never felt alone, though. The memory of those happy times flickers past my eyes now in a kaleidoscope of feeling.

Being by this stream makes me feel young. I feel young in a way that only the wind in your hair can make you feel. I feel close to you, too.

Often it's as though you're beside me, your spirit dancing as free and uninhibited as the wildness of the natural world that you loved so much.

It was here that I first told you about Christopher. I told you how our friendship grew into trust and then very steadily into something more. I told you also that he would never replace you in my heart. No-one will ever begin to do that.

Christopher was the one person to whom I felt I could really talk about the harder, darker moments of losing you.

Your illness progressed so quickly that there wasn't time to prepare.

There was just a stunned numbness that your future was dissolving faster than valley mist in the sun's morning rays. And then, slowly, the realisation dawned that there was only the present for us now — that there could be no future any more . . .

I remember you saying with a brave hint of laughter in your voice that the present was all anybody ever had anyway.

Then eventually there came a time when you were past words, when you reached out your hands towards me, your beautiful eyes more eloquent than all the things you could no longer say.

The worst thing about the funeral was the solid walls of the coffin. The walls you hated, closing around you with impossible finality. I only survived the ceremony because Christopher held my hand and kept whispering over and over that you were free now.

That same afternoon I came here to stand by this stream and to carry out your last wishes. You didn't want to be part of the ground, but of the air, of the soft Fernriver air.

And so I set you free on the warm summer winds.

SLOWLY, I turn and walk back along the stream. Christopher's waited long enough, today and every day these last five years. He's helped me to piece my life back together with a patience that matches your restlessness.

He's the one person who seems to have understood that losing your twin is like losing one half of yourself. He's helped me very slowly to put back the pieces until now I feel almost complete again.

As I reach the top of the slope, I can see his car. I can picture him inside, biting his lip, his dark hair falling over his eyes as he pretends to read the paper, pretending that my pilgrimage doesn't worry him in the slightest.

I run the last few steps to the car and he looks up, surprised. I smile and climb in beside him, shaking the wind from my hair.

He doesn't speak, but he reaches across for my hand; no pressure in his touch, only gentleness and understanding.

I know from his expression that he can sense something's changed: that today, at long last, I feel at peace and, for the first time, I'm holding nothing back from him.

I watch the uncertainty in his eyes slowly clearing and with a hint of the telepathy that I'd only ever known with you, I know that soon he'll say, "Marry me, Lisa."

And I know that this time I'll say yes. ■

A Wonderful Wedding

by Sheila Ireland

Everything was going so smoothly — even so, he couldn't help remembering another day and a wedding that was over before it had begun . . .

THEY couldn't have asked for a better day for the wedding, Matt Brady thought, standing there at the altar.

He grinned reassuringly as his best friend came to stand alongside him. Jeff returned his grin and gave him a covert thumbs-up sign. Then they both straightened their shoulders and gave their attention to the minister in front of them.

It was quiet inside the village church but for the self-conscious giggles of the children dressed in velveteen and lace and silk and the church organ softly playing.

The whole village had turned out for the wedding but they all waited in hushed silence.

Matt swallowed and touched his lapel. He felt enveloped by his rented tuxedo and wondered if his bow-tie was straight.

The organ stopped playing. Matt held his breath and leaned forward slightly, shifting his weight from his heels to his toes. Then the opening bars of the Wedding March came swelling through the organ pipes above the altar.

Matt raised his head but resisted the urge to look around. He could feel his heart beat.

Sarah would be coming down the aisle now at her father's side, walking slowly with the music.

She would be a beautiful bride, just as she had always been beautiful to him. Even when they were just kids everybody had said that they were meant for each other . . .

Matt smiled, remembering.

As it happened, the only people who had had any doubts about that were himself and Sarah. Old history now but at the time it had been important, more important than anything had ever been before.

★★★★

Of course, most people would have put it down to pre-wedding nerves or plain stage fright, for it had happened on the night of their first wedding rehearsal. In fact, he had confessed as much to Jeff, later that night.

"What do you mean you're not sure?" Jeff had looked at him sharply, astonished. "Matt, you're crazy. Sarah is one in a million. Some blokes would give their right arm to marry somebody like that and you . . . ?" He shook his head. "Look, mate, the rehearsal has got you spooked, that's all. It'll be different tomorrow, you'll see."

He had walked home with Jeff's words ringing in his ears, glad of the advice. But lying there in his bedroom at three o'clock in the morning, not able to sleep, he had known it was more than that.

It wasn't the rehearsal at all, it was the real thing that worried him.

Did he really want to marry Sarah?

In the grey early light of the morning, that question had frozen him like a sliver of ice.

He could not imagine a life without Sarah, and yet . . .

He had sat up in bed, chilled, suddenly angry with himself. How could he doubt his love for Sarah?

She had always been there for him, right from the start. She had been born six months after him, in a house only a stone's throw away.

When they were toddlers they had held hands and helped each other walk, while their parents laughed and smiled and said, "Bless them."

They had played in sandpits together, and made mudpies and memories. They had shared their secrets and their dreams, through kindergarten, primary and high school. And when they were seventeen they had carved their names on the big oak tree in the park.

What was he worried about, he'd asked himself. Sarah and he had been children together. Now they were adults. In two more weeks they would be married.

It was what they'd always wanted . . . wasn't it?

The question had been deep and disturbing and remained unanswered, for just then the phone had begun to ring downstairs in the hallway.

★★★★

Now, standing in the church, Matt became aware of the swish of silk and satin and the scent of fresh flowers. He turned his head and saw that Sarah was standing close to him and smiling beneath her bridal veil.

She was stunningly beautiful, just as he'd always known.

Her blue eyes were warm and clear and confident and so unlike the eyes he had seen on that pale, early morning — it seemed so long ago now — when she had phoned and asked to see him . . .

★★★★

"Sarah, what's wrong?"

"Matt, I need to see you. We have to talk." Sarah's voice was shaky and urgent and a bit high-pitched, as if she had been crying.

"All right, Sarah. Take it easy. I'll meet you in the park. Our bench, by the oak tree. All right?"

IT had been a cool, silvery morning with a fine mist hovering over the park and the first faint tints of pink beginning on the horizon.

After Sarah's call, he had dressed quickly in his tracksuit and trainers and jogged all the way, working on an instinct to be there first, to reassure Sarah that she could depend on him, no matter what.

He had sat down on the park bench and stared at the oak tree with their initials carved on it, the past seemingly very clear — it was the future that was hazy. Then Sarah had appeared from around the hedgerow on the corner.

She was wearing her blue tracksuit and her blonde hair looked very pale in the early light. She wore no make-up and looked younger than her eighteen years.

He had risen to meet her and quickly put his arm around her shoulders.

"Sarah, what's the matter?" he'd asked when they'd sat down.

She had looked at him and blinked and shook her head.

"I don't know, Matt. I don't know if I can go through with it. The wedding, I mean." Her voice trembled.

"I love you, Matt, but I don't know . . ."

She'd looked bewildered, like a child lost in a supermarket or a maze, and afraid. And it was strange because he had known exactly how she felt. Even now he could still remember. All he felt was a sense of relief.

"It's all right, Sarah," he'd said softly. "It's all right."

Her doubts had allowed him to give voice to his own and he had told her how he'd been unable to sleep, worrying about the same thing.

She took his hand. "What are we going to do, Matt?"

He'd looked at her but said nothing. They couldn't just call the whole thing off, could they? Up until now their lives had been so smooth and predictable, filled with easy decisions.

This was different. They couldn't rely on the past any longer.

"It's not just ourselves, Sarah, it's our parents. They've been looking forward to our wedding for ages."

"For years."

"Maybe we're not ready. Maybe we're too young?"

"The wedding invitations have been printed. Mum's already posted off a lot . . ."

"The banns at the church . . ."

"The wedding presents . . ."

"The reception hall . . ."

The fell silent, awed by the enormity of their thoughts. Slowly then, they began to talk. And it had been in those moments, just as a new day dawned, that they made their decision to cancel the wedding — to wait and be sure.

"Mum will be furious," Sarah had said.

"So will mine," Matt replied.

"They won't understand."

"It's hard."

"But we can make it up to them later," Sarah had said quickly, and there was a new firmness in her voice then. And she smiled. "Later, when we are sure . . ."

★★★★

Matt blinked now and glanced quickly across at Jeff as the minister coughed softly, and began the wedding service. "Dearly beloved, we are gathered here . . ."

Looking back, he knew he and Sarah had made the right decision. They had had to be sure, and their happiness today was proof enough for anybody.

At the time, though, it had all come as a bit of a shock and he'd known that he had to get away.

You can't throw a spanner like that into the workings of a small village and not cause ripples of confusion. Call it great expectations, curiosity, concern or just plain nosiness, but people just couldn't let things lie, so when the opportunity came up he'd taken it and gone to live in Canada.

He hadn't severed the link, though. He had kept in touch with Jeff and it was about six months later that Jeff had told him he was going out with Sarah . . .

Matt smiled now, just the way he had smiled when he'd got that letter, for in his heart of hearts he'd known that something like that might happen, and he was glad . . .

"Matt, the ring!" somebody whispered urgently.

He looked up to see the minister smiling at him.

"Sorry." He grinned foolishly at Sarah, then took the wedding ring out of his pocket and gave it to Jeff.

He felt a bit foolish. He'd never been best man at a wedding before and he'd known it might be a little strange. But when your best friend — your two best friends — ask you to be best man at their wedding, what can you say?

Matt smiled softly as he watched Jeff slip the ring on to Sarah's finger, and then he couldn't help himself. He glanced around and smiled at his wife and baby son, sitting in the front pew of the church.

Yes, Sarah, he thought. We did the right thing. ■

A Creative Christmas!

Christmas is the season for creative cross stitch, and we're sure you'll love our festive projects.

Angel Delights!

Our cheerful angels grace sachets that can be filled with potpourri or dried flowers. Look out for potpourri mixtures with delightfully spicy Christmas scents.

JOY ANGEL SACHET

29

YOU WILL NEED

JOY ANGEL SACHET
- Cream/gold Lurex thread
14-count Aida 13 cm (5¼ in) square
- Contrasting fabric 13 cm
(5¼ in) square for backing
- 56 cm (22 in) of 6 mm (¼ in) twisted cream and gold cord
- Three small red fabric hearts (optional)

LOVE ANGEL SACHET

LOVE ANGEL SACHET
- Antique beige 14-count Aida 14 cm (5½ in) square
- Contrasting fabric 14 cm (5½ in) square for backing
- 60 cm (24 in) of 6 mm (¼ in) twisted red and gold cord
- Small red and green tartan fabric star (optional)

FOR EACH SACHET
- DMC stranded cotton (floss) as listed in the key
- Tapestry needle size 26
- Small amount of filling
- Small amount of potpourri
- Clear glue or mini glue dots
- Sewing machine or usual sewing equipment

30

Key To Angel Delights

DMC Stranded Cotton
Cross Stitch (2 strands)

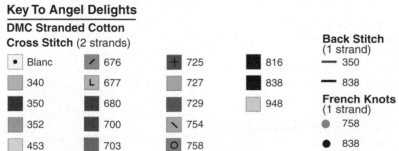

• Blanc	✦ 676	✚ 725	■ 816
▨ 340	L 677	▨ 727	■ 838
■ 350	▨ 680	▨ 729	▨ 948
▨ 352	■ 700	＼ 754	
▨ 453	▨ 703	O 758	

Back Stitch
(1 strand)
— 350
— 838

French Knots
(1 strand)
● 758
● 838

31

1 Find and mark the centre of the Aida. Starting in the centre and following the chart, work the cross stitch for your angel in two strands of embroidery cotton.

2 Work all the backstitch and French knots in one strand of the colours shown in the chart.

3 With right sides facing, pin the stitched piece to the backing fabric. Stitch together all round, taking a 12 mm (/2 in) seam and leaving an opening at the bottom. Clip the seam allowance at the corners, turn the sachet out and press. Stuff firmly with wadding and push a small amount of potpourri into the centre. Do not close the opening yet.

4 Neatly stitch the twisted cord to the edges of the sachet, making a small loop at each corner as shown. Use the opening at the lower edge to conceal the ends of the cord and then slipstitch closed.

5 If desired, attach the fabric star or the hearts with a spot of clear glue or use mini glue dots.

Something Simple
Our charming gingerbread house project is particularly suitable for a beginner.

YOU WILL NEED

- Pale lemon 14-count Aida 36 x 36 cm (14 x 14 in)
- DMC stranded cotton (floss) including two skeins of white as listed in the key
- Tapestry needle size 26
- Mount board and picture frame

Design size 21 x 20 cm (8¼ x 8 in)
Stitch count: 114 high x 110 wide

1 Find and mark the centre of the Aida. Starting in the centre and following the chart, begin by working the cross stitch in two strands.

2 Work all the backstitch and French knots in one strand of 838.

3 When you have completed all the stitching, wash and press your work and prepare it for framing.

We used a lovely bright shade of lemon as the background for this

design. The colours of the gingerbread show up particularly well against it, giving a lively look and making this design suitable as a year-round picture for a child's room.

Key To Gingerbread House

DMC Stranded Cotton

Cross Stitch (2 strands)

● Blanc	762	911	975	3706
321	801	╱ 913	977	3801
— 415	838	955	3078	3826
○ 3855				

Back Stitch (1 strand)
—— 838

French Knots (1 strand)
● 838

33

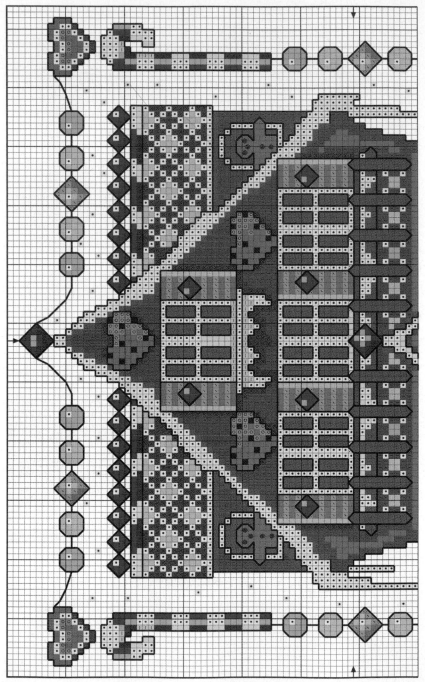

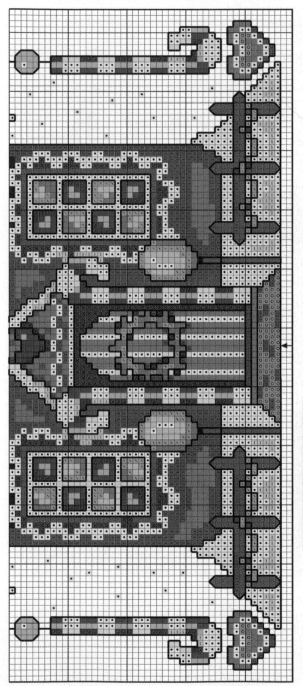

Credit Line:
Taken from Sue
Cook's Christmas
Cross Stitch
Collection, published
by David and Charles
@ £18.99. Copyright
© Sue Cook 2005.

You can order the
book for the special
price of £16.99 plus
free p & p (UK only).
Please call 0870
9908222
or email dcdirect@
davidandcharles.co.uk
and quote code Y755.

An Unlikely Matchmaker

by Isobel Stewart

As cats go, he was pretty rough and ready.
He was also a true romantic...

A REMARKABLE woman, Great Aunt Hester — a terrific organiser." Sally had often heard her father say that, with a mixture of admiration, affection, and perhaps just a touch of awe.

She felt the same mixture of emotions now, as her mother's voice came down the phone-line at her.

"Great Aunt Hester wants me to do what?" she asked, incredulously.

"She wants you to stay in her house and look after her cat, while she goes to Cousin George's funeral," her mother repeated.

"Why me?" Sally said, putting up at least token resistance.

"You're the only relative in the area," her mother pointed out reasonably. "And besides, Hester says the cat really took to you."

Sally had visited Great Aunt Hester three times since she came to work in Birmingham a few months ago, and she had to admit that the cat, a snow-white prize Persian called Princess, had settled herself on Sally's lap on each visit, leaving a legacy of fine white hairs on everything Sally had been wearing.

"You'd be able to get a train to work," her mother went on. "And it would only be for a few days . . ."

Sally shared a flat with three other girls, and she had to admit the thought of a bathroom all to herself had some appeal. Besides, she was fond of the old lady.

"All right," she agreed.

★★★★

The next day was Saturday and Sally rolled up at Great Aunt Hester's with a suitcase about midday.

Hester's house was in a row of renovated old cottages with tiny rooms and tiny gardens.

"I'm very grateful to you, Sally," Hester said briskly. "My bag's packed, and I'll just be on my way." She shook her head. "Can't think why George had to go and die. He was only seventy-two, you know.

"Never was much staying power in him, though," she sniffed. "Even as a boy, he was a quitter."

Sally looked at her great aunt to see if she was serious. She was. Hester herself was 80. A former teacher who'd never married, she was in the same robust good health as always.

"Now, you know where everything is," Hester went on. "I've cancelled my private tuition pupils so it's only Princess and you."

Princess looked up from her cushion and yawned, her topaz eyes half-shut.

"You must never allow her out in the garden alone," she told Sally.

"But I'm away all day, Aunt Hester," Sally pointed out. "What if she needs out?"

"She has her Arrangements," the old lady said, nodding to a litter tray. Then, gazing out the window, she stiffened slightly.

"Ah, there he is," she said accusingly.

There, strolling nonchalantly across the garden, was a large black and white cat.

He was sturdy and raffish, and it was obvious from his rather tattered ears that he had been involved in a few scrapes.

Hester rapped on the window.

The tom cat looked up.

Hester rapped again.

Unhurriedly, the moggy strolled across to the high wall, jumped up on it, and sat there, licking one paw, eyeing the old lady sardonically.

"I never had any trouble about letting Princess out, until he moved in next door," Hester said.

She lowered her voice conspiratorially. "I think he has Designs on her. So don't ever let her out alone. If you're with her, you can just chase him away."

THE confident tom was still there long after Great Aunt Hester had gone. Sally went out into the garden — carefully shutting Princess in — and spoke to him.

He was, she couldn't help thinking, much more her sort of cat than the aloof and dignified Princess. He jumped down from the wall, rubbed against her legs in a very friendly way, and then rolled over so that she could tickle his tummy.

"You're a rascal, aren't you, Ivan?" Sally remarked. "I'm very sorry I can't invite you in for a saucer of milk, but maybe we can speak to each other like this sometimes."

"I wouldn't trust him an inch," a voice said from the top of the wall.

Startled, Sally looked up to see a young man with thick, fair hair, blue eyes, and a cheerful smile.

"Hi."

"Hi," Sally replied. "I was just . . . er . . . talking to your cat."

"I know — I heard you. He likes attention. Here, cat, come on home. Stop bothering the nice lady."

"What's his real name?" Sally asked.

"Just cat," the young man said and his eyes crinkled. "What did you call him?"

"Ivan," Sally admitted, a little embarrassed. "I once had a cat just like him . . . a terrible character. Ivan the terrible," she added fondly.

"Right!" he chuckled. "My name's Jeff — Jeff Harding. I'm a lawyer," her neighbour volunteered.

"I'm Sally Wilson, and I'm a secretary," Sally said.

She explained that she was looking after her great aunt's house for a few days, and that she had been given strict instructions that Princess was not to be allowed out because of next door's cat.

"Oh, your aunt's quite right — his intentions are extremely dishonourable," Jeff replied cheerfully. "Like I said, don't trust him an inch. Me, now, I'm your traditional, trustworthy, clean-living, boy-next-door, and I'll do my best to keep this disreputable animal away. Be seeing you . . ." He paused. "Soon?"

Sally's heart lifted. A neighbour like Jeff was something she hadn't expected when she'd agreed to look after the cottage and the cat.

THE next day was cool but sunny, and Sally enjoyed herself exploring the well-tended beds in Great Aunt Hester's garden. Princess watched her, eyes narrowed, from the window.

Sally felt sorry for her, so she brought her out.

Five minutes later, however, like Errol Flynn in an old movie, Ivan the second, as she'd come to think of next-door's cat, leapt agilely down from the wall, confident and dangerous.

Sally scooped Princess up in her arms.

"I really am sorry," she told Ivan, and she wasn't sure whether his expression was a smile of acceptance, or a leer of intent. But he took no offence, and after Princess was safely inside, he stayed beside her, stretched out languidly on the grass.

"You wouldn't happen to have any sausages, would you?" Jeff peered over the wall.

"Sausages?"

"I thought we might have the first barbecue of the year — unless you have anything else planned?" Jeff suggested.

Sally had planned an omelette and salad, but she instantly rejected that.

"A barbecue sounds lovely, but I don't have any sausages." Mentally she ran through the contents of Great Aunt Hester's fridge. "I think I've got some hamburgers, though."

"Great! Bring them over."

★★★★

Jeff's garden and his cottage were as tiny as Great Aunt Hester's.

"I'm only renting this place," he told Sally, "but I prefer it to a shared flat."

The hamburgers were delicious, and so were the fried onions and the baked potatoes, which they'd cooked in the microwave.

The only slight problem was the distant faint protest from poor Princess, safely and sadly shut in her own home.

"I think I'd better get back and keep her company," Sally said at last, regretfully. It was dark, and she could think of nothing nicer than whiling the evening away with Jeff in his cosy candlelit sitting-room.

"Thank you, that was much nicer than having an omelette," she told him.

"Are you good at making omelettes?" Jeff enquired.

Sally nodded. "Not bad."

"Maybe tomorrow night I could come round and we could have omelettes, and keep Princess company?" he suggested.

"OK," Sally said. "You're on."

And from then on they took it turn about to cook for each other, sharing stories, jokes and laughter.

On the Thursday, Jeff took both Sally's hands in his.

"I'm so glad we met," he said softly.

"So am I," Sally murmured.

Jeff kissed her then, very tenderly.

"See you tomorrow night?" he asked her, his voice not quite steady. Sally nodded, her eyes shining with happiness.

But they were to meet sooner than that . . .

SOMEWHERE in the middle of the night, Sally was woken by a terrifying wailing, loud enough to raise the dead. Nervously she pulled on her dressing-gown, and ran through, barefoot, to the tiny living-room. Even in her fright, she noticed that Princess's cushion was empty.

Her eyes flew to the window. She'd opened it an inch when she'd got back from work to let in some fresh air, and she'd obviously forgotten to close it. Surely Princess couldn't have . . .?

But Princess had.

She was outside in the garden now, and Ivan was with her . . .

Just as Sally flung the door open, Jeff shot over the garden wall and scooped up his swaggering pet.

Meanwhile, Sally took hold of Princess. "Are you all right, baby?" she asked.

"Depends what you mean by all right." Jeff raised an eyebrow.

In the moonlight, they looked at each other. There was no need to say any more.

"I'd better shut that window," Sally said at last.

"Bit late for that now," Jeff said ruefully. "Lord knows what we'll tell your aunt."

The next night, Great Aunt Hester phoned.

"You wouldn't believe how foolish I've been, Sally," she said before Sally could tell her about Princess. "Gone and broken my ankle — rather badly it seems — and young Dr Thornton says I've got to stay put."

Waves of relief washed over Sally.

"Don't you worry about a thing, Great Aunt Hester," she said warmly, trying not to feel guilty. "You just look after yourself, and I'll stay on here."

"Could be weeks," Hester warned.

All the better, Sally thought.

"How's Princess?" her great aunt asked.

Sally swallowed. "Princess is — just fine," she said.

It wasn't a lie, she told herself. Not really. I mean, just look at her; lying on her cushion, a picture of sheer contentment.

No. Princess was fine. Just fine . . .

A week later, Sally took Princess to the vet, who confirmed that she was pregnant, and gave her some vitamin tablets.

Sally paid up and left, with Princess purring steadily inside her basket. One thing was for sure, she thought, as she drove home in Jeff's car, borrowed for the occasion, there was nothing stand-offish about Princess now.

She adored Sally, she adored Jeff, and, now that their brief and passionate romance seemed to be over, she and Ivan had become very good friends, too.

★★★★

The weeks went by, and Princess blossomed. Sally and Jeff's friendship blossomed, too. In fact, there was only one cloud on the horizon: what were they going to say to Great Aunt Hester?

"With luck," Sally said hopefully, "it could all be over. The kittens could be born, we could find homes for them, and she might never know."

Certainly, young Dr Thornton was still insisting that his patient couldn't travel. And — sooner rather than later — Princess would have her kittens. Would they get away with it?

One evening, Sally came home from work, and there was no sign of Princess. Her heartbeat quickened. Surely she hadn't left the window open again!

Just then Jeff arrived.

"She'll be hiding somewhere," he assured her. "Probably getting a little nursery ready. I'll help you to find her."

Jeff was right. After five minutes, they found Princess lying on a bed of sweet-smelling linen in the airing cupboard, surrounded by a wriggling bundle of kittens.

Absurdly, Sally felt her eyes fill with tears, as the beautiful cat purred and stretched her claws blissfully.

"You darling," Sally said softly. "Aren't you a clever little mother?"

They decided not to disturb her but went back to the kitchen and solemnly drank a toast in cooking sherry.

Two days later, Princess allowed them to inspect her family. There were four fluffy black and white kittens, and two mostly snow-white, but with little dark flecks.

"They're beautiful, your babies," Sally told the cat, then turned to Jeff. "If we could only have another month or so, we could find homes for them. They could go at six weeks, couldn't they?"

"Oh yes," Jeff agreed. "I've got two folk in the office who'd be interested in taking one. You've got a couple more. Yes, I'm sure we'd manage — provided your aunt stays away."

Sally smiled weakly. "Fingers crossed . . ."

Luck did, indeed, seem to be on Sally's side, for two weeks later there was still no sign of Great Aunt Hester. Then suddenly one Sunday evening, there she was in the driveway, waving to a car that had just driven away.

"Sorry I couldn't let you know I was coming," Great Aunt Hester apologised, giving her a kiss on the cheek. "But Dr Thornton's boy, Mike, was driving down this way and he offered to give me a lift. It was a spur of the moment thing."

Sally swallowed. "Aunt Hester," she began, "there's something . . ."

But just then, Princess strutted along the corridor.

"There's my Princess, and she looks as beautiful as ever," the old lady said, and she picked up the cat, and held her close.

When she put her down, Princess rubbed against her legs, and then walked along the corridor, looking back imperiously at her mistress.

"Look at her," Hester said fondly. "She's telling me something, wants to show me something."

You bet she does! Sally thought inelegantly, bowing now to Fate, as she followed her great aunt and the cat into the spare room . . .

THE cupboard door was open, and the kittens were playing on the floor, in the part Sally and Jeff had fenced off for them.

Great Aunt Hester stood for a long time looking down at them.

Sally waited, unable to think of anything to say. Her aunt's shoulders were shaking, but she didn't say a word. Sally felt awful. Was Hester so upset that she was crying?

"Aunt Hester?" she asked tentatively.

Her great aunt turned round, tears of laughter streaming down her face, her mouth upturned in a broad grin.

"No need to ask who the father is!" she said, lifting up one of the black and white kittens.

"The window was only open an inch," Sally said. "I really never thought she could get out, but —"

"But she did," her great aunt finished for her.

"We've found homes for four of them," Sally told her eagerly. "They can go in another two weeks."

"We?" Hester asked her.

Sally felt her cheeks grow warm. "Jeff and I . . . he's Ivan's — the cat next door's — owner," she said.

Her great aunt's eyes rested thoughtfully on her.

"Hm," she said, with a great deal of meaning. And then, briskly, "Well, I knew I should have had her spayed. As soon as the kittens go, I'll see to that. I think I'd like one of these little black and white fellows, though. They're gorgeous!" She rubbed Princess's ears. "Well, you've had your fling, my girl, you'll just have to live on memories from now on."

A sudden, surprising thought came into Sally's head. Was it possible that Great Aunt Hester had some memories herself? Memories that made her more understanding than Sally had dared to hope she might be?

"Well now, I've brought back some country ham," Great Aunt Hester said. "What about you asking the young fellow next door to join us? Looks as if he could do with some feeding-up."

"Yes, Great Aunt Hester," Sally said meekly, laughter bubbling up inside her.

And as she stood at the door waiting for Jeff, she thought, with rising happiness, I have so much more than memories. I have so much to look forward to.

I have Jeff.

A well-built, scruffy shape came rushing from somewhere along the road to greet her.

And I have Ivan, she thought.

"Sally?" Jeff said anxiously, opening the door. "That's not your aunt back, is it?"

"It is," Sally told him. "But everything's fine, Jeff — she even wants to keep one of the kittens!"

She took his hand. "She wants you to come and have supper with us," she said.

"Are you sure?" Jeff said doubtfully.

"Quite sure," Sally assured him.

And quite sure, too, she thought, that Jeff and I are at the start of something very wonderful, and very special.

At their feet, the cat miaowed.

"Thank you, Ivan," Sally said. "Thanks for everything, you terrible, lovely moggy!" ∎

In Lilac Woods

by D.Galton

We've shared so many tender memories here. I just hope my letter can help us rediscover that happiness . . .

DEAR Ellen, In the beginning you were always saying you loved me, and I was always saying it back. I guess that's what people do in the early years.

Do you remember when we first met? The times I would cycle over to your parents' house and we'd sit in the garden, chaperoned by distant eyes watching from the curtained windows.

The only chance we really got to be alone together was when we went walking in the lilac woods that backed on to your parents' garden. I've thought about those walks often these last few days.

Do you remember how the weather didn't matter? Summer or winter, we'd chase across the fields, intoxicated by the raw freedom of it all, into the quiet welcome of the trees.

We were like lots of couples the world over. We grew together, brought up our family together, became comfortable across the years with the absolute familiarity of each other.

And then you started saying you loved me less often, and I didn't say it at all.

It didn't stop overnight. There was a gradual decline and, if I'm honest, I can trace the beginning of that decline back to the time I was made redundant.

At first I was shocked, numb right through with disbelief, and you were sympathetic and supportive.

"It's not your fault, Jim," you'd say, over and over, your brown eyes all soft with love. "It's happening everywhere — it's not your fault."

Somehow it was worse when the fact that I was no longer bringing home a wage had sunk in. Some people withdraw into themselves, give up. I didn't. All I could feel was this furious, bitter anger.

I'd worked so hard. I'd believed in the company, believed in what I was doing, and their, Please don't take this redundancy as any reflection on your work line, just made me all the madder.

The trouble was, that soon that fury started to spread within me. Little things started to irritate me — things that you did, things that our Danny and Janice did, even when they were trying to help.

Like the time Janice brought me that job advert from the paper. I thought she was patronising me. How can you go from being a transport planner to a bus driver? I mean, where's the parallel?

I didn't mean to snatch the scrap of paper out of her hand. I didn't mean those scathing remarks. It was just a reaction, but I know that all the apologising in the world doesn't take away the hurt.

I knew it even as I shouted at Janice. I felt guilty for shouting at her, I really did, but I couldn't seem to stop myself.

It's like a disease, bitterness is, creeping through you like arthritis, stiffening you up, overriding all sense of normality.

REMEMBER the day our Danny landed that promotion in the printing shop? He came home all bright-eyed and told you out in the kitchen, quietly, because he didn't want me to hear, didn't want to rub my nose in it.

There was this air of tension the whole evening because he couldn't find a right time to tell me . . .

I mean, I couldn't blame the lad. I knew he was only trying to be diplomatic. You all were, but somehow that made it worse. It made me wonder what kind of father I'd become, not being able to accept my own son's success.

Redundancy wrecks lives. They say that, don't they? Like the adverts they used to have on television: Drinking and driving wrecks lives.

But I haven't done anything wrong, or at least I hadn't, not up until the redundancy. It's since then that all the trouble's really started, isn't it? I feel like I've wrecked our life, isolated you, scared the kids.

Somehow I've pushed away the three people who are the most important to me.

I know you didn't understand when I said I needed a few days' quiet — a few days away from you. It wasn't meant to be a rejection of you, Ellen — of any of you. It was just me being hurt and not being able to cope with it.

I felt like I'd destroyed so much of what we'd built together over the years. I just knew that I had to get away before I destroyed it completely.

I don't know if you can understand that. I'm not sure I could understand if it were you who'd run away. I guess I've had a lot of time to think over these last few days — a lot of time looking at the same four walls of this bed and breakfast place.

I never knew a room this small could feel so empty. But the thinking's helped, it really has. It's given me a chance to put things into perspective. A chance to come to my senses, if you like, to let all that anger and bitterness come out of me.

I never was one for fancy words, Ellen, you know that, but I feel a lot more clear-headed now. I feel that I've got the anger part sorted out at last, that I can see everything properly.

I can't say I like what I see, either.

You were right, Ellen, when you said I was being selfish. I was lashing out at you, when I should have been letting you help, but I was too proud, wasn't I?

Mrs Spriggs (she's the landlady here) said something this morning that made me think. I've not told her, of course, what I'm doing here.

I've just said I'm staying here while I try to find work, that as soon as I've got something organised, my wife will be coming to join me.

At least that's what I told her when I first came, but it's only a small place, you see, and Mrs Spriggs does like to chat, and I don't think she really quite believed me.

Anyway, this morning she served me my boiled egg and she said, "It doesn't come cheap, does it?" Just that: "It doesn't come cheap," and she blushed a bit, as if she thought she may have overstepped the mark.

To be honest, I didn't cotton on at first. I thought she was talking about the breakfast or something, and I just shrugged. And she raised her eyebrows and glided off to see to another guest.

It was only afterwards when I went back to my room, that I realised she must have meant pride.

So what I'm trying to say, Ellen, to you and Danny and Janice, is that you were right. Redundancy isn't the end of the world, and getting a job isn't the only thing in life worth thinking about.

Maybe I'll get work again soon, maybe I won't. Perhaps we should sit down and talk about that market gardening idea you had.

The one thing I do know is that I'm not going to waste any more time in anger and bitterness. It doesn't solve anything.

I love you. I love the girl I used to walk with in the lilac woods, and I love the woman I've grown up with across the years.

I know you can't blot out what's happened. It would be impossible now, in any case, but what I'm asking is that you'll give me the chance to try to make it up to you.

I know it's a big thing that I'm asking. I've hurt you all so much. I have no excuse for it and I'll understand, truly I will, if you think it's too late. But please don't say it's too late, Ellen. Please, let's start again together.

Please say it's all right for me to come home . . .

All my love,
Jim xxx ∎

*A poem by Joyce Stranger,
inspired by an illustration
by Mark Viney.*

THE LOST DREAM

*High on the hill as I look down
I see the edge of the huddled town.
I come here always on the day
That you left me and went away.
We were so young, and life was sweet
All the future at our feet.
I'd visions of walking by your side
Away from the church as your new bride.
I designed my dress . . . I chose the flowers
Plans for our home filled my waking hours.
I turned towards you to share my dream
Of our future shaped in the sun's bright gleam.
You sat and watched a boat on the sea
And I suddenly knew you weren't listening to me.
All your thoughts were far away
You hadn't the least desire to stay
Within the confines of the little town.
You didn't want to settle down.
Three weeks later I stood alone
Watching the boat as you left home.*

My world for years was dim and grey
But then my Johnnie came my way.
We married and had children born
Yet if we came here I felt forlorn.
Today is different. I don't know why.
The sun shines bright in a deep blue sky.
The same boat dances across the sea
And at last I know you were never for me.
So many tears and wasted years,
But now, at last, I feel I'm free.
I forget the boat and hurry down
For all that I need is there, in the town.

"Just For A Change"

by Teresa Ashby

As the holiday loomed, Sam knew that this year things *had* to be different . . .

"WHAT do you think of this one, Sam?" Hal chuckled. "Listen, if finding chocs is your desire, take five long steps east of the fire. Look left, look right, look straight ahead —"

"Hal," his wife, Samantha, broke in softly, "I've been thinking . . . about Easter."

"I hadn't finished," he said, his eyebrows vanishing beneath his mop of fair hair. "I was just getting to the best bit."

"I don't want to spend Easter at your mother's this year," Sam blurted out.

"What?"

Sam felt a flame of colour burn in her cheeks. It had taken ages for her to pluck up the courage to say it.

She'd wanted to say it last Christmas, and the one before. Last Easter, too — and their wedding anniversary and every one of Tom's birthdays from his first right through to his fourth in February.

But somehow, the words always stuck in her throat before she managed to say them.

It wasn't that she didn't like Hal's mother. Far from it. She was the kind of woman it was impossible not to like. It seemed only natural that the whole family should gather at her house for all the big celebrations — and most of the little ones, too.

At first it had been fun getting together with all Hal's brothers and sisters and their various partners and offspring, but now it was getting tedious.

Just once, Sam wanted to have her own little family to herself; to be able to cook a celebration meal for the four of them, even if Katie's did have to be mushed up and fed to her on a spoon.

"I thought you liked my family." Hal looked perplexed.

"I do," Sam reassured him. "But . . ."

She wanted to voice her reasons, but maybe Hal would think she was being small-minded.

Was it such a crime to want to spend time alone with the ones you loved most in the world, she wondered?

She'd come from a big family, too, but it had been an unwritten rule that once you left home and started a family of your own, you became a separate unit.

Oh, they'd rally round if anyone needed help, and now and then they'd get together if there was something big to celebrate. But not on every occasion.

"You know it's a family tradition," Hal went on. "The Easter egg hunt straight after lunch, the late afternoon walk . . ."

"The hot cross buns for tea, the games of charades in the evening. Oh, Hal . . ."

How could she possibly explain that, nice as the gatherings were, they didn't hold the same charm for her as they did for him? Besides, beneath the fun and jollity, there were always family tensions.

His sister, Abbey, unable to have children of her own, always seemed uncomfortable around babies. Was it only Samantha who noticed the pain in the girl's eyes every time her mother dumped yet another squirming bundle in her lap?

There were other little niggles and arguments, too. No, it wasn't all fun and laughter, not by a long chalk.

"I always hide the eggs and set up the clues," Hal said softly.

"You still can," Sam said eagerly. "We can have our very own Easter egg hunt right here at home."

"It won't be the same," he said miserably.

Sam's patience ran out. She'd hoped he'd understand. But whatever happened, she wasn't going to give in over this.

"Well, you spend Easter with your mother if you like, Hal," she said angrily. "I'm spending it here, at home, with my family!"

★★★★

It was a hollow victory, and Sam felt dreadful when, later, she heard Hal murmuring into the phone.

"Yes, I know. I'm sorry, Mum, but we've decided to spend Easter at home this year."

Sam could imagine Molly sitting on the red-carpeted stairs at home, clutching the phone, tears of hurt welling in her eyes.

"All right, Mum," Hal went on. "Yes, I'll do that."

"Do what?" Sam asked, when he'd finally hung up.

"She wants one of us to pop over some time to pick up our eggs."

"I'm sorry about this, Hal," Sam said, reaching out to touch his arm. "But I really think —"

"Yes," he interrupted, shrugging off her hand. "I know what you really think, Samantha."

Sam sighed. She knew this was the right thing to do, but it looked set to remain a bone of contention between them for some time to come.

LATER, when the telephone rang, Sam answered it and recognised Abbey's voice on the line. Her heart sank. Was she about to receive one call after another from Hal's family, telling her how unreasonable she was being?

She took a deep breath. "Hello, Abbey."

"I bet it was your idea not to go to Mum's for Easter this year."

"Yes," Sam admitted defensively.

"Good for you! She took it so well, I dared to suggest that Bill and I needn't go either.

"I couldn't bear it, Sam," she went on. "You know what it's like — especially now Gemma has had another kid. It'll be one baby after another thrust at me — as if somehow that could make me produce one of my own!"

"Oh, Abbey, you mustn't let something like that come between you and your family. I'm sure your mum isn't trying to —"

"I know she means well," Abbey said kindly. "It's just that Bill's been wanting us to go skiing at Easter for years."

"So you're going away?"

"Certainly are," Abbey said, her delight obvious. "Austria! I feel as if a huge weight has been lifted off my shoulders."

When Sam related this news to Hal, he threw up his hands in despair.

"Well, that's it then. Easter at Mum's will be a complete wash-out."

"And it's all my fault, right?"

Before he could reply, the telephone rang and Hal snatched it up.

"That was my brother," he said when he'd finished. "Apparently as we're not going to Mum's, they're not going to bother either."

After that things got worse. Hal's grandparents decided to book themselves on the Autumn Rompers Club's Easter coach trip to Bournemouth, and his Uncle Dennis plumped for attending a reunion of his regiment in Birmingham.

One by one, the families that normally gathered at Molly's house cried off. And it was all Sam's fault — or so you'd think, to hear Hal talk.

"Poor Mother," he muttered. "She'll be all alone at Easter. She's never been alone at Easter — never!"

"She won't be alone, Hal. She'll have your dad."

"But the family won't be there," he complained, "and you know how she likes to cook a massive roast and organise games."

"Last Christmas I found her near to collapse in the kitchen," Sam said softly. "I wasn't going to tell you, Hal, but . . . well, she's not a young woman any more, you should realise that.

"Don't you think it's time you let your parents have some time to themselves?"

Hal looked thoughtful.

"Put like that, you may have a point," he said eventually. "I've been silly, haven't I?"

Sam smiled. "It's never silly to care," she said.

EASTER was much as Sam had planned. She brought Hal breakfast in bed — accompanied, of course, by Tom, her little helper.

They spent a leisurely morning together and, after lunch, went for a walk in the park.

Sam linked her arm through Hal's as he pushed Katie in her buggy and Tom ran ahead, looking under all the bushes for the Easter Bunny.

Sam felt good inside — except for one small, niggling worry: was Molly all right, or was she feeling lonely and rejected?

Hal, she was sure, was wondering the same thing, but neither of them said anything until after tea. Then, Hal cleared his throat and, with an almost embarrassed grin said, "I was, er, wondering how you'd feel about strolling over to Mum's to see how she's getting on."

Sam smiled. "Mummy's boy," she teased, but she wasn't cross. "I think that's a good idea."

Hal hugged her. "I knew you'd understand," he said. "I've had a terrific day, loved every minute of it. Just the four of us."

He looked thoughtful. "We don't often spend a day together like this, do we, Sam?"

"Not often enough," she agreed.

"From now on, it's us first — right?"

"Right," she said, warmth flooding through her.

★★★★

"What's going on?" Hal said, as they approached his mother's house. Cars were lined up in the road outside and all the lights were blazing. "Looks as if Mum had her Easter party after all."

Sam felt a stirring of unease and she grasped little Tom's hand tighter.

Hal rang the bell and it was his younger sister, Gemma, who flung the door open.

"Where have you —?" she began, then stopped when she saw who it was. "Oh, it's you. I don't suppose you've seen our parents anywhere, have you, Hal?"

"Why?" Hal manoeuvred the buggy into the hall and parked it with the others. "Are they missing?"

"I'll say." Abbey appeared from the kitchen. "Bill twisted his knee on the slopes, so we came home a day early.

"We thought we'd pop in to see Mum and Dad, but when we got

here, the house was cold and deserted. I let myself in with my spare key."

"We just thought we'd call in and check they were all right," Gemma put in, "and found Abbey and Bill here on their own."

The rest of the family had much the same story to tell. Molly's house was full of people — but there was no sign of Molly herself!

Much later, with the smaller children packed into the huge, old, Victorian cot upstairs, the adults sat downstairs, twiddling their thumbs, pacing the floor and looking out of the window . . .

Then, shortly after midnight, they conceded defeat and went to bed.

It was just like other Easters. Children chattering into the small hours, adults wrapped in sleeping bags, babies cuddled up together.

Only the most vital ingredients were missing: Molly and Jack.

"Maybe I should call the hospitals," Hal said, sitting up suddenly in the dark and almost knocking Sam off the small sofa bed.

"You think there might have been an accident?" she murmured sleepily. "I hadn't thought of that. Perhaps it wouldn't hurt to call round."

They crept out into the hall to find Abbey had beaten them to it. "I've just called all the local hospitals and they don't know anything," she said fearfully.

"I'm making some more tea." Gemma appeared from the kitchen. "Anyone else want one?"

"This is ridiculous," Hal said as the hall clock chimed three. "We all decided not to come here so we could spend more time with our own families — and look what happens! Look where we end up."

"This is all my fault," Sam said apologetically. "I started all this."

"It's not your fault." Abbey was the first to reassure her. "You simply had the guts to do something we've all wanted to do for years.

"It's not easy to break with tradition like that, but we've got to grow, to change."

At last, and only when the first light of dawn started to trickle through the curtains, the family went to sleep.

WHAT'S all this?" Jack gasped as he turned into their road early that morning. "Look at all the cars, Moll!"

"What on earth . . .? That's Abbey's car . . . and Matthew's, too . . ."

"I wonder what's up?" Jack mused.

"I knew it," Molly tutted as she got out of the car. "The one day I decide to let my hair down and enjoy myself, some crisis happens!"

They crept into the silent house. The lounge was full of sleeping people, so were all the bedrooms.

"I'd best put the kettle on," Molly sighed. "Then we can wake this lot up and find out what's been going on."

LATER, when everyone was sitting sleepily clutching mugs of tea, Molly explained where they had been.

"Your dad surprised me," she said, squirting maple syrup over a home-made flapjack and handing it to Hal. "Woke me up at the crack of dawn yesterday and announced we were off to France for the day!

"France! We had lunch in this gorgeous little restaurant." She went starry-eyed for a moment. "It was so romantic.

"He always promised to take me to France for lunch, but somehow, we just never seemed to have the time . . ."

Jack winked at her. "Plenty of time, but none of it ours — until now."

"You could have let us know," Gemma said sulkily.

"Oh, yes? When you lot were stirring your stumps, we were halfway across the Channel! Anyway, I didn't think you'd be so worried."

"And you didn't get back until this morning?" Abbey asked.

"Late last night actually," Molly said, a secretive gleam in her eye as she looked across the kitchen at her husband. "We booked into a little boarding house and got up early to watch the sun rise over Beachy Head."

"Beachy Head!" Hal spluttered.

"It's where your father proposed to me all those years ago," Molly said, smiling lovingly at Jack. "Years and years ago . . ."

Sam looked at Hal. His mouth had fallen open. He turned to look at her and began to laugh. She'd been right all along. Dear, sensible Sam. What would he do without her?

There'd still be family occasions, huge parties, great times, but from now on, they'd make room for themselves and their own little families — and for Molly and Jack, too.

He reached out, took Sam's hand in his and gave a little squeeze that meant I love you.

She squeezed back, I love you, too.

And only Molly's happy sigh disturbed the sudden, contented stillness that had fallen over one big happy family. ■

Time To Herself

by Marian Hipwell

Perhaps here she could learn to look forward and not back . . .

YOU'LL be all right?" Paul asked her anxiously. Shelia looked around, abstractedly. Apart from the caravan, the only other building was the converted farmhouse, discreetly hidden by overhanging bushes. To the other side was a meadow, home to a flock of sheep.

There were no people — no-one to keep up a pretence for . . .

"We'll be fine," she told him.

There was a fleeting look in his eyes then, a loneliness which reached out to her but found no response.

If she had given a sign, he would have stayed, she knew, made some excuse to his office. The moment passed.

"I'll see you on Saturday then." He brushed her lips with his. "Look after yourselves." A swift hug for Suzanne, then he was striding back towards the car while they watched him from the caravan door.

"'Bye, Daddy." There was uncertainty in Suzanne's voice. She didn't understand why he wasn't staying with them, despite the fact they had explained it wasn't their real holiday, only a chance for Mummy to get away from things.

"What things?" she had wanted to know.

Paul had looked at his wife helplessly, not knowing how to reply.

"Mummy needs some time to herself," he had said at last. And Shelia hadn't been able to contradict him.

When the car had disappeared from view down the lane, she turned to go back inside, pausing when she caught sight of Mrs Groves from the house, briskly cheerful and ready to be friendly.

"If I've forgotten anything in the caravan, Mrs Rogers, just let me know." She smiled at Suzanne, watching her from behind her mother's skirts.

"Hello, love. You'll like it here. It's pretty peaceful," she explained, looking back at Shelia. "Though the sheep might keep you awake a bit until you get used to them."

"We'll be all right," Sheila said. She didn't sleep, anyway.

The sheep were moving now, in single file, down to the far meadow. It made a strange picture to her town-bred eyes.

Now I know where they get the saying "following like sheep", she thought.

"The lambs get separated from their mothers in the dark," Mrs Groves was explaining. "That's what all the noise will be about."

Sheila was conscious of a stab of pain. Mrs Groves couldn't know the pain that statement would cause her, of course. Paul wouldn't have divulged anything so painful, so personal, to someone they hardly knew.

"Right, then." Mrs Groves turned back to the house. "Malby's only a mile down the road. It's a nice place to visit. And it looks as if you'll be lucky with the weather."

Shelia murmured something appropriate, relieved when the other woman hurried back to her busy life.

"Can we go down to the sea, Mummy?" Suzanne asked.

"If you like, dear."

Shelia looked down at her daughter.

The last few months had been hard on Suzanne. She had found it as difficult to respond to the child as she had to Paul. He understood, but Suzanne was only five.

All she knew was that her mother didn't hug her as much as she used to, didn't laugh with her over funny pictures in her books, didn't even seem like her mummy at all . . .

THERE was something in the peaceful country scene which greeted Sheila as she looked out of the window until the sun had dropped down below the horizon.

She felt cold then, alone suddenly in a way she hadn't felt for ages. Drawing the curtains, she switched on the television and stared at it until it was time to go to bed.

"They didn't bother you then, the sheep?" Mrs Grove was out hanging her washing when they emerged from the caravan the following morning.

Shelia shook her head. "I can't honestly say they did."

She had only become aware of them when the pathetic bleat of a lamb intruded into the morning stillness, reminding her suddenly, achingly, of the first cries their baby had made.

Padding across to the window, she had looked out at the pale dawn, seen the lamb wandering round.

Find your mother, she had urged silently. Find her, before you get separated forever . . .

She hadn't allowed her thoughts to linger on that day at the hospital for ages; told herself it was best not to look back.

But looking forward hadn't been the answer, either. Because all the future showed was a gap where the baby would have been.

So often she had walked quickly past mothers pushing prams, averted her eyes, tugging Suzanne along with her. The child hadn't been able to understand why the baby brother she had been waiting for had gone away so quickly.

"Didn't he like us, Mummy?" she asked anxiously, when Shelia had tried to explain.

"He loved us just as much as we loved him," Shelia had told her. "He couldn't help having to go away.'

Even then, in the face of her daughter's bewilderment and childish sadness, she hadn't been able to cry. She had shed her tears for the baby the morning he died; the same morning he was born.

Since then, there had been emptiness.

Would she walk around, feeling nothing, for the rest of her life? The thought frightened her.

Paul had been wonderful. Despite his own grief, he had been her rock, her shoulder to lean on. Yet lately she'd caught a look in his eyes which told her he didn't understand.

He had grieved, still did, but had returned to his man's world of work and relaxation, carrying his sadness in his heart, not allowing it to dominate his life. As she had, his eyes said.

It was time now for her to come back to them. Learn to cry again, feel again.

It was pleasant and mindless at the caravan, a way of passing time. They explored the surrounding area, visited the fair. They took a boat trip, sailed past a colony of grey seals, heard the shrieks of cormorants and kittiwakes as they nestled on the rocks of the wild life sanctuaries; places where humans couldn't go.

I'm like that, she had thought suddenly. I'm on a rock somewhere, so high no-one can reach me. And I don't know how to get down . . .

ON their fourth night, the sheep were nosier than usual. She lay awake, listening to the plaintive cries.

"Yes, they were worse than usual," Mrs Groves agreed, when Sheila remarked on it. "They took the lambs away, you see, yesterday. Whilst you were out. They say the sheep don't know, but they do."

"I didn't realise." Sheila stared at her uncomprehendingly. She noticed then there were hardly any lambs left in the meadow.

The pain of grief was there again, in her heart, sharp in its intensity, just as it had been before the numbness had taken over and held her powerless in its grip.

She murmured something to the other woman and hurried towards the caravan.

She couldn't shut the cries out, though, the terrible, heart-rending bleating as the sheep mourned the loss of their lambs.

Tears ran down her face then. It was as if a dam had opened up; as if all the pain and sadness of the last few months had saved itself up for this moment.

She cried as if her heart would break, only pausing when she felt Suzanne tugging frantically at her skirt.

"Mummy?" There was fear in the child's voice, which communicated itself through the pain.

"Don't worry, love," she tried to say, yet it came out as an incoherent gasp which frightened the child all the more.

She held her then, rocked her in her arms, willed her to believe everything was all right. It wasn't true. But it would be . . .

The numbness was ebbing away and she was coming down from that high place. Suddenly, her thoughts went instinctively to Paul, waiting so patiently.

"Let's go down to the telephone box," she told Suzanne unsteadily. "We'll ring Daddy, ask him to come."

The child danced by her side as they hurried down the lane. Daddy was coming. Everything was going to be fine.

"Shelia? Are you all right?" Anxiety tightened Paul's voice.

"Paul —" She stopped, took control of the tears threatening to overwhelm her again. "I love you," she said at last. When only silence greeted her, she panicked. "Paul? Are you there?"

"I'm here." His voice was husky suddenly. "I'll clear my desk and come right down."

THEY were waiting for him as he drove up the lane that evening. Shelia watched as Suzanne dashed towards him and he picked her up and hugged her. Then he stepped forward, setting Suzanne carefully down, and Shelia hurried into the arms he held out, enjoying the familiar reassurance of his strength.

"I've missed you," she said. His arms tightened round her, told her he felt the same. Not just for this few days, but ever since the morning that had been their baby's lifetime.

They stayed a few days longer, but were all eager to go back home.

When they left, the Groves waved them off, non-plussed by their early departure, Shelia guessed, and not really convinced by the excuses she had made.

As they drove down the lane, Shelia turned and looked back. The sheep were peaceful again, huddled in groups, quietly grazing. They had accepted their loss. Accepted, but not forgotten.

For her, the acceptance was more gradual, but it was coming.

She looked up at the sky then. Already, there was the promise of a beautiful day. ■

Wild and Free

by Dorothy L. Garrard

His taste for garden produce was a problem. But luckily, Rabbit's taste in people was impeccable!

THE man appeared suddenly at my back door, which startled me, since he must have come along the alley, and up my long back garden. I was making jam at the time and the back door was wide open.

Determinedly I tightened my grip on the saucepan handle, ready to repel this grumpy-looking stranger who was stomping his way up my path. As he got nearer I realised he wasn't in fact a total mystery-man, but my new neighbour, who'd moved in two weeks ago, and whom I hadn't met yet.

The closer he got, the more I wished it could stay that way. He was looking most unneighbourly.

Fixing me with what was probably his most serious expression, he said gravely, "Your rabbit has eaten all my peas!"

It wasn't quite the opening gambit I had been expecting, and I suppressed a nervous desire to giggle.

I hadn't seen him this close before. Chunky, with brownish hair, his round wire glasses added character to his unremarkable features.

"What makes you think it's my rabbit?" I enquired.

"Because I saw it from my bedroom window. It hopped out of your gate, along the alley and straight into my garden. It knew exactly where my peas were. 'Were' being the operative word!"

His blue eyes glinted indignantly and I tried to remember what Daphne, our Residents' Association treasurer, had told me about him. According to her, his name was Les Denton. He was in his early 40s and rather unsociable.

Mentally, I added a few descriptions of my own: short-tempered and fanatical gardener. Our grumpy Mr Denton must have planted those peas before he even laid his carpets.

"You're saying Rabbit had a plan of action?" I remarked now. "I know rabbits are intelligent, but still . . . couldn't you have shooed him away?"

"He practically stripped that row in the time it took me to get downstairs — and he's already had several cabbages. With the best will in the world, there's not much I can do to stop him."

At this point my jam erupted like Vesuvius. This did not surprise me.

Since my husband had done a runner with someone younger, prettier and more indulgent of his ego, life had been even more chaotic than usual. With an inward groan, I turned off the gas.

"Look," my visitor said, realising he couldn't compete for my attention with an avalanche of foaming jam, "just admit you're responsible for that animal and try to keep him in your own garden — OK?" He turned and stalked away without waiting for my reply.

Everybody seemed to be able to do that except me, I thought, as I watched his retreating back. With a sigh, I looked round for something to mop up the mess.

THE next day — Sunday — at about half past twelve, Rabbit hopped his way up my path again. I was busy chipping yesterday's jam disaster off the stove at the time.

I was wearing a baggy cerise T-shirt which my daughter had given me when she got her figure back after her second baby.

Les Denton, by contrast, looked exceedingly smart when he arrived on the scene some twenty minutes later, as if he'd been to church.

Perhaps that accounted for his expression of determined Christian forebearance.

"It occurred to me that I didn't see a rabbit hutch or run when I was here yesterday, Mrs Kelland . . .?"

"No," I agreed, scoring off some enamel with the knife tip.

"But you must do something about it! Surely other neighbours complain?"

"As a matter of fact, nobody else has. They've mostly turned their gardens over to lawns and patios for barbecues, or gone green and wild, like me." I nodded at my Amazon-like garden with its authentic jungle atmosphere.

"Rabbit must have chosen you like he chose me," I went on. "I came downstairs one morning and there he was, peering into my kitchen through the glass in my back door."

"But he must belong to someone!"

I shrugged. "I put the cards in shop windows, an advert in the local paper, and stuck 'Lost Rabbit' posters on all the lampposts in the area, but either that 'Someone' is holding their peace — probably with good reason, seeing as how he's so destructive — or Rabbit migrated from Watership Down."

Les Denton's expression was growing more bemused by the minute.

"I'm afraid I babble when under stress." I sighed. "Rabbiting on, my husband used to call it . . ."

A few laughter crinkles appeared round his eyes, and he suddenly looked much more human. But all he said was, "Can't you confine Rabbit to the shed? It's quite big."

"I'm afraid it hasn't got a door."

"Wire netting?"

"He's not mine to keep, and I don't like shutting animals up. Anyway, I know nothing about rabbits and I haven't the time to look after him. If I let him run loose, he can at least forage for himself." At that I broke off, embarrassed, and Les Denton looked at me ironically.

"That's precisely why I'd appreciate your co-operation, Mrs Kelland. It's OK for you, but that animal is denuding my garden quicker than a plague of locusts!"

"Actually," I said mischievously, "he hasn't been back since yesterday. He's obviously decided he's better off over at your place."

I rather enjoyed his look of consternation.

"I'd offer you some jam by way of compensation," I said sweetly, "but once it gets out of the jar it runs faster than Rabbit. I'm afraid everything I do seems to be a disaster at the moment. Still, if Rabbit comes back, I'll have words with him."

"Er — thank you," Les Denton said uncertainly. He looked completely nonplussed, and for a moment I also felt sorry for him.

O N Monday evening, just after I arrived home from the newsagent's where I worked, Rabbit came bounding up my path with a carrot between his teeth, scurried into the shed and sat nibbling frantically.

He was far too busy to take any notice of the wood and wire contraption guilt had made me knock together, and I stapled this rather rickety "frame" to the door of the shed.

Ten seconds later, Les came galloping after him. In contrast to his elegance of the previous day, he now wore a suit, no tie, one shoe and only a sock on the other foot. In his right hand he brandished a hoe . . .

"You're not going to clobber him with that," I said, hammering determinedly at the frame in an effort to prove that Rabbit's adventures would not be going on for much longer.

"Ouch!" I sucked my throbbing thumb.

"Maybe not, but you're going to demolish your shed with this if you're not careful!" he returned, taking the hammer out of my hand and using it more scientifically.

Rabbit watched until the carrot poking from one side of his mouth and the greenery dangling from the other had been minced up, then swaggered over and leaned his weight on the wire.

Several staples fell out, and Les threw down the hammer in disgust.

Pleased with himself, Rabbit retreated back into the shed to wash the remains of Les's garden from his face.

"I'll tell you what," Les offered, "if you can let me have some of that netting, I'll knock up a frame myself and bring it round."

I didn't really have any option but to agree to his suggestion, and when he'd gone, I wagged my finger admonishingly at my charge as he happily digested his meal.

"Well, you got what was coming to you," I told him. "You have to learn that you can't just go around helping yourself to whatever you fancy."

Rabbit gazed back, unconcerned.

Next morning, before I went to work, I took out some vegetable scraps and dropped them through the small gap at the top of the frame. Usually this prompted a frantic scrabbling, but this time no Rabbit appeared.

"Come on now," I chided, "stop sulking. I know it's not as fresh as the stuff you've been stealing from our friend Mr Denton's, but it's all you're getting for now."

Silence . . .

Intrigued, I loosened the top to peer in. All I could see was daylight through a displaced slat of wood at the back of the shed, where Rabbit had made good his escape . . .

Les came round dutifully after work with a neat job in wire shed doors. He groaned when he saw the hole, and, after examining the rickety state of the shed, said Rabbit-proofing was out of the question.

"Well, don't even suggest me buying him a hutch," I said flatly. "Rabbit's far too big and active. He could give a greyhound a head start."

"I know," Les said drily.

I scratched my head. "It's a poser all right," I admitted eventually. "But the least I can do is to ask you in for a coffee while I pay you for the frame, anyway."

"Forget that —" Les waved a hand dismissively " — I had stuff lying around. But I'll take you up on that offer of coffee, thanks."

In the kitchen I moved a heap of newspapers off a chair and wished I'd put on decent trousers after work instead of Sally's comfy but crumpled jeans.

Suddenly I realised that my self-respect had gone to pot. I was a slob.

Take last Saturday, for example.

I'd been trying to give up biscuits, but late on Saturday night I'd thrown together a cake which had stayed where it was put in the bottom of the tin until I'd dug it out and gobbled half of it at one go, hot and indigestible as it was.

I put the sorry remains on a plate now and looked at them, embarrassed.

"I'd still fail Domestic Science even after all these years of being a mum," I said awkwardly. "Don't risk it if you don't want to."

Les Denton smiled gently to himself, but didn't say anything. He just seated himself in the rocker.

He took a piece of cake. "I like rocking chairs. I like your kitchen, too. It's homely — interesting."

"You do?" I was astonished. "It's been a dumping place for years, for everything I can't bear to part with."

"Maybe, but it's better than an empty barn like mine. Is that a photo of your daughters?"

"Yes, Stephanie and Sally. Stevie works abroad, we meet when we can. Sally married a Welshman, and their farm keeps them too busy to visit much. My barn's empty in another sense. It must be something I said."

Les gave a faint shake of his head and asked abruptly, "And what are you good at?"

"Good at?" I looked at him blankly.

"Yes, good at. All I hear is self-deprecation. Your cake and jam aren't fit for human consumption, you can't hammer in a nail, control a garden or even a rabbit. The things you like best make your kitchen a dump and it's even your fault that your family grew up and left!"

He sounded surprisingly angry. "Listen, I'll tell you something. Twelve years ago my fiancée literally left me at the altar. I was in my thirties before I met her, and I absolutely adored her.

"But she eloped with my older brother, who was good-looking, clever, a local sports hero and a real go-getter. The way they did it had a romantic gloss that made even that seem less awful — to everybody except me!

"After it happened, I got drunk a good deal — not a normal occurrence, I'll have you know — and I shed buckets of real tears. It seemed the only thing to do.

"Because I was so desperate, I began tackling things I'd never thought of doing before, just to take my mind off it, and one day, light dawned.

"I'd always lived in David's shadow and taken it for granted I could never be like him, but it was only then, in my darkest hour, that I realised I'd missed the point.

"There was no need for me to be like David or anybody else — only like me. It was only when I began to explore what I could do that I discovered any measure of self-esteem; that I realised I was just as good as the rest."

He smiled at me encouragingly. "It's obvious someone's got at you on the same subconscious level. But you're attractive, you've got sensitivity and a great sense of humour, and ringing up two well-balanced girls in the framework of a rocky marriage is no mean feat.

"You're not inferior — you're Ann Kelland; unique, and every bit as good as anyone else . . ."

I was stunned into silence and Les Denton looked embarrassed.

"I'm sorry — I got carried away."

"The all-knowing Daphne told you my life story, I suppose?"

"She filled me in on everybody — whether I wanted to hear it or not. But it wasn't just what she said. It was hearing you — seeing you taking everything lying down. It reminded me of myself a few years ago."

"Well," I swallowed. "Thanks. I mean — really, thanks."

Les cleared his throat. "What I've said — it was very personal."

"I promise your life story won't get back to anyone else."

"What a relief, thanks a lot!"

We drank our coffee, visibly wondering where to go from here.

"By the way, how's the thumb?" Les asked politely. "It looked sore yesterday."

"It's OK. I'm not too bad at —"

I paused and corrected myself to saying something more positive. "First Aid's something I'm very good at. I took courses and got certificates. My daughters were both real tomboys — they seemed to spend most of their childhood dicing with death!"

He laughed aloud and I liked the sound so much, I went on.

"I can draw, too. I wanted to go to Art College when I was younger, but then I got married instead." I rooted around in one of the kitchen drawers.

"Here's the original drawing I did to stick on the lampposts for Rabbit's owner, featuring Rabbit in the flesh — or rather, in the fur.

"And I've a set of hand-bells in the broom cupboard, but they irritated Gordon so I stopped practising." I looked at him breathlessly.

"All this is making me thirsty," I said. "I don't know about you, but I could do with some more coffee."

"That sounds like an excellent idea; and do take up the bells again. I'm into the heavy artillery myself. I've only been here a couple of weeks, and I've already been roped in as standby bellringer at St Mary's."

Later, I saw him off down the garden path in the summer dusk. Rabbit sat under my favourite rhododendron, shampooing his ears.

"Your side fences are high and sound," Les mused. "Suppose I could shut off a decent area for him with that strong, green covered wire?

"Think about it, Ann." His voice was as gentle as the whispering of the summer breeze.

NEXT morning, that same rhododendron was shaking like a harebell in a hurricane. I inspected Rabbit's excavations with disbelief and dismay.

Suddenly all Les's tribulations came sharply into focus. I rang him straight away.

"OK," I said. "You get your way. Let's go for that fence . . . and pronto!"

Les needed no second bidding, and like a pair of highwaymen we lay in wait until Rabbit ventured back into my garden, then we rushed round with the wire netting and securely fastened him in. Our joy knew no bounds. Rabbit explored the perimeter with interest. Then he gave us a pitying stare, gathered himself together, took a galloping run and a flying leap, and, with a contemptuous flick of his powder puff, he was over the top.

Les gave a low whistle. "He certainly does hate captivity," he mused. "I wonder if you guessed right about him being wild? But where could he have come from?"

"The undeveloped land the far side of the motorway?" I hazarded. "That's nearest, and there's open country beyond it. What if he managed to get across and is too frightened to go back?"

"We could take him there and see how he reacts," Les agreed. "But first we've got to catch him!"

We looked at each other and started to giggle.

★★★★

On Sunday, using Les's few remaining carrots, we finally trapped Rabbit in a wooden crate from the greengrocer's. Les carried the struggling box to his car and we raced off to the footbridge a few miles away.

Before we'd got halfway across the bridge, Rabbit was squeezing himself out. He leaped ahead, raised himself on his haunches, pricked his ears — then bolted.

We waited, eyes on the green beyond the high bank and the hedges and trees while the traffic whizzed by underneath us.

"I suppose we could hardly expect him to wave goodbye," I said at last. I felt surprisingly forlorn considering only a few days previously the creature now streaking across the fields below us had come close to destroying my favourite bush.

Les placed a consoling hand on my shoulder. "I think he's gone home," he said eventually. "I'll bet the whole warren's waiting to hear Big Chief Rabbit's Amazing Adventures. He'll dine out on stories of peas and carrots for years to come."

"You're getting as daft as I am!" I said.

"It's the company I keep," he grinned. "I like it. Come on, how about these two exhausted humans finding a pub and getting a bit of Sunday lunch? I'd invite you back to my place for dinner, but I've no vegetables left!"

His hand still lay lightly on my shoulder. It felt good.

"That sounds great," I said. "Just so long as you promise me you won't order rabbit pie!" ∎

A Daughter's Tribute

by Sheila Ireland

My father gave me nothing but love and understanding, and in return I brought him heartache . . .

TODAY, sitting in the small church where I was baptised, I cannot stop myself thinking of my father and of the years that have gone before.

I keep remembering the love, understanding and joy he brought to my life, while I was often only a source of heartache and disappointment to him.

The church organ is playing softly. The congregation is still and expectant, waiting for the vicar to take his place and begin the service. But in my mind's eye I can see my father smiling gently, patiently, the way he did when I was small.

Funny, it is only now that I can truly appreciate his patience. Back then, when I was a child, all I ever wanted to do was test it.

Now I can see it was a gift, but a hard-earned one. Few men could have put up with so much, I think.

You see, Dad always wanted a son, but instead, he had five daughters, me being the last in the line. That must have been a lot to swallow for a man who loved fishing, football and snooker.

71

Mum and Dad baptised me Joanne, but my father called me Jo. In his mind, I think he always added an "e" on the end.

Maybe that was part of the trouble . . .

Somehow, I think I knew from the start that I was the only one in the family who could make things up to my father. The one who could compensate for him never having a son. The trouble was that there was never truly a Joe. There was only ever a Joanne . . .

THE organ is playing "Rock Of Ages", the favourite hymn of the fishermen of our village.

Even when he wasn't working on the trawler out in the North Sea, my father loved to fish, mostly from under the big oak tree on the riverbank down by Westbrook Fall.

From the time I was a toddler, I tagged along. But I was never any good at fishing. Dad tried to teach me, just as he would a son, but I always got my line snagged or a hook caught in my finger.

My sisters never caused him that much trouble. They were all older than me and more drawn to my mother's ways. More normal, I suppose.

Dad never let me go with him on the trawler, though, because he said it was much too dangerous for a "young 'un". I had to be content with waiting on the pier for him to come home at the end of each day.

I was more trouble to him than any of his children. Always pestering, always being a nuisance, always around him even when he probably didn't want me to be. Dad never complained, though.

"I'm your father, Jo," he told me once. "Whatever you want to do with your life, I am here to help you, remember that."

I did remember. It was like a promise and I tried to make it into a pact.

I knew if Dad had had a son, he would have wanted him to become a marine biologist. I'd often heard him talk about the fine work those people did. So I decided that that would be my part of the bargain.

IN the church, I sigh very softly as the organ falls silent. The congregation stirs, as if a breeze has just passed.

People raise their heads expectantly but I am motionless, remembering the bewilderment in my father's eyes when I came home from university, after only one year of my studies in marine biology, to tell him I was getting married.

I had already written to my parents about Paul, but I think my father simply could not believe that the love I spoke of was anything more than a teenage friendship. Until that night . . .

"Why now, Jo?" He swallowed hard. "You're only nineteen. Can't you wait a bit — until your studies are over?" His voice was gentle but nervous, and I could hear his disappointment, feel his pain.

"No, Dad," I said. "We can't wait. We have to get married . . ."

He lowered his head, his face pale, and I knew I was breaking his heart.

"Do you love him, Joanne?" he asked quietly.

"Very, very much, Dad." My voice shook and I tried desperately to stop myself crying.

My father took me in his arms and said, "Hush now, love. We've got things to talk about, you and I." He raised my chin gently with his fingers and smiled. "We've got a wedding to arrange, haven't we?"

NOW, in the church, the vicar has come forward and I know it is almost time to begin the service. As I glance at my husband, Paul, sitting alongside me, he takes my hand. I bow my head and remember the night of the storm, when my father's trawler failed to make it back to harbour and I was left waiting, windswept and soaking wet, on the end of the pier.

The seas were treacherous that night and I knew the entrance to our little harbour was complicated by underlying currents and subject to freak waves. They could easily whip up and tip over a craft as small as my father's trawler.

Though I'd shivered, the fear inside me was more chilling than the weather. Suddenly, I was so terribly afraid that my father might not be returning, not now, not ever.

I wished desperately, for the very first time, that I might truly have been Joe and not Joanne, and that I could have been out there, alongside him, helping.

My father deserved a son.

I stood crying abjectly until Paul and my mother came, put their arms around me, and took me home.

No-one slept that night. We listened to the storm blow itself out. And in the first light of the morning, we returned to the harbour, to wait and pray.

At a little after seven, we saw my father's trawler on the horizon, chugging a straight and true course for home.

★★★★

Paul squeezes my hand now and I look up to see the vicar beckoning us. He walks forward to the small christening font and I gently pass our baby into his arms.

My father and mother come to stand alongside us. And I meet my father's eyes and smile as the vicar baptises my son and names him Joseph. ∎

*Blaze had been a special dog, a born winner.
And looking back, the old farmer realised that
his own life had been special, too . . .*

Once Upon A Memory

by Joyce Stranger

P OOR, old boy," people said, when they saw Dan Armitage sitting in the sun in his wheelchair. "It must be terrible for him, not to be able to walk, or talk, or go anywhere. Even at ninety . . ."

Dan couldn't talk, but he could hear and he could communicate, as the care assistants who looked after him knew very well.

He could thank them for their help, with a little smile and a gentle tap on the hand.

One tap meant yes, and two taps meant no, and an irritable drumming meant that he didn't like whatever was being done or said.

However, he was very rarely irritable. He had been a widower for many years and was quite self contained, enjoying his own company, and that of his farm animals.

People might pity him, but he was rarely in pain, and though the stroke that disabled him so badly prevented communication, he enjoyed observing the life that went on around him.

He learned long ago that acceptance provided more bonuses than railing at Fate.

Fate had not been kind in his younger years, and it was not until some years after his wife died that he found a way of making the farm profitable.

There was money enough now to ensure that he could be looked after at home by agency carers and a son next door, who made sure that all was well with the arrangements.

He was surrounded by his own familiar comforts, and though he no longer lived in the farmhouse, the cottage he occupied was on his own land and, of course, there were the animals . . .

He could derive endless pleasure from watching the lambs playing, the sheepdogs working and the more immediate comfort of the three Siamese cats, last of the line his wife had bred.

Tai and Sanso and Chloe seemed to take it in turns to honour him with their company, lying tucked against him, purring softly, making a music that enchanted him.

Another enchantment was his son's first granddaughter. Her childish chatter was endlessly entertaining and her large, solemn eyes were replicas of his late wife's.

Little Emma herself listened to the adults round her, pitying her beloved great-grandfather, but her five-year-old mind couldn't believe that he was unhappy.

TODAY was a red letter day, a rare, fine day with the sun warm enough to take the chill from Dan's old bones, shining across brilliant fields under a clear, blue sky.

He could hear the background babble of the stream that slivered its way over rounded rocks, where he had so often caught fine trout, which Alice had grilled to perfection.

It was Jack who had bathed and shaved, dressed and fed him today. Then he had wheeled Dan out of doors into the sheltered corner of the kitchen garden that always caught the heat.

Now he sat in dappled shade near the edge of the shadow cast by the big ash tree that had been planted the day his elder son was born.

Both his sons were over 60 years old. It didn't seem possible. Where had all the time gone?

Odd to think of his sons as grandfathers themselves and semi-retired, too. John had passed over the management of the farm to his son.

Charlie, Dan's younger son, had left the farm to become a successful solicitor. While his two daughters had pursued quite different careers in the art world; Jane as an animal illustrator, and Sara as a writer.

Suddenly little Emma tapped his hand very gently, recalling him to the present.

"You can hear me, can't you, Granpa? Daddy says to tell you that Maggie had twin lambs. Jack says he'll push you round to see them.

"You'd like that, wouldn't you?"

She watched the hand that said yes, saw the vivid blue eyes brighten, and the little smile that was all that his old face could manage, and she nodded confidingly before going off again, leaving

Dan with his memories. And they were such memories. Between dozes he could re-live the grand days again, and recapture the elation of those times.

Like the day Alice promised to marry him. They had been walking on the high hills, on a frosty afternoon; the grass and trees were glittering and snow capped the mountains.

He saw it so clearly. The white and the blue of the countryside and the vivid face of the girl who had gladdened his life for nearly thirty years.

He could see her still, laughing as she always was in memory, her black curls cascading from under the jaunty scarlet cap that reflected the colour in her cheeks.

He could still look at the photos of their wedding day, and remember her walking towards him in a cloud of white.

The birthdays of his two sons were just as vivid.

The first time he'd held each tiny baby in his arms, looked down at the small faces, he'd felt the same passionate love overwhelm him.

Those sons and their families comforted him in his old age with their care and concern for him. They were good men — both of them — and had married good women.

The grandchildren were grown, too, and this little one, his great grandchild, was an added blessing.

THOUGH he didn't always remember clearly what had happened the day before, parts of the past were so clear that he could live them again.

He tasted in retrospect the wonderful roasts that he could no longer eat even if Alice were there to prepare them.

The light on the grass reminded him of the marmalade she made each year. "Trapped sunshine", as he had once described it, in a rare moment of poetry.

He could see the rows of jars, the wonderful translucent golden colour and Alice's proud face as she lined them up on the pantry shelf.

No-one made marmalade like that any more.

Oh, yes, there was a lifetime of memories.

He glanced at the wall where flowers patched the moss and the sheepdog lay.

She, too, was a memory, a shadow, yet he could see her so clearly — the open, laughing mouth, thick gleaming black coat in contrast to her white legs — and of course the white blaze down her nose.

She seemed to him to be there still, growing more solid every day. At first she'd appeared just as a shadow, a thought, but lately she'd become as real as when she had lived, so many years ago.

His favourite, she'd been. Blaze, he called her, because of that white mark between her wise eyes. Such a dog. A once-in-a-lifetime dog.

Alice had bred her and given her to him on his fortieth birthday.

"A pup to win with," she'd said, as she kissed him. He could see her standing there, no longer young.

And Blaze . . . Oh, many other dogs had nudged his knee, but she'd been the best of all.

She'd won the cups that young Tom polished so lovingly and set before him every week, seeing the brightening of the old man's eyes.

He was Dan's youngest grandson, already beginning to make a name for himself at the sheepdog trials.

He'd watched with pride last year as Tom had won the novice class at the local competition.

A chip off the old block, the shepherds said, coming to pay their respects to a man who was himself a legend. The only one of his day left alive.

His mind drifted through the years to the roars of applause as time after time he and Blaze won every trophy possible in the sheepdog trials.

She was a wonder, a miracle, a dream of a dog, and no other dog had ever reached her standard.

Other dogs had been defeated by wayward sheep, but Blaze mastered them, eyeing them so that they turned and walked where she drove them, never putting a paw wrong.

They were such a team, he and his little dog. And always at the edge of the crowd was Alice, watching, willing him to win.

"Good lass," he'd say, and Blaze would lean against his leg, almost purring like a cat.

LITTLE Emma was running through the fields now, as once he had run, so long ago, before men had ever thought of walking on the moon; before they'd invented machines that brought pictures of the world into the living-room.

Sometimes he wished he could tell his family the thoughts that occupied his mind and helped to pass the days, so that they did not waste pity on him. He had little need of it.

Day succeeded day and he was glad to wake in the morning and savour the little things that pleased him.

Suddenly his thoughts returned to his childhood and he was a tiny boy, lying in bed, his parents arguing above him.

"He'll catch a cold."

"Rubbish," his father had said robustly, and wrapped him in his dressing-gown and two thick blankets before carrying him outside into the winter night.

He must have been very small because he'd been able to cuddle up in his father's arms, feeling the rough tweed of his jacket, and the day-old beard that scraped his cheek.

It was a full moon. They stood by the old plum tree that seemed to raise its arms to the sky in prayer.

As they watched, a darkness came and the moon began to vanish, and soon they were standing in the dark, cold night, not a spark of light anywhere.

"It'll come back, lad," his father said. "I always think of the light as God's promise to us, telling us that, no matter what troubles we face, there is light ahead.

"The darkest hour is the one before the dawn. Whatever happens to you, little son, never give up. Never despair . . ."

It had been awesome there in the deep night and he hadn't understood the words, but he'd felt safe and cherished and warm.

He understood them now though . . . There had been many black times, but always there had been hope and finally the good times had returned.

He had never forgotten those words . . .

There was another vivid memory, too, of his mother showing him a rainbow for the first time. She'd described it as God's promise of fine weather after rain.

He had never feared the God who made rainbows and eclipses and the wonderful animals that graced his farm.

At the end, he knew, God would take him home

WHEN his thoughts finally returned to the present, the sun was hidden by a small cloud and it was much cooler now. Soon they would come to take him in.

There was the evening television to look forward to. He loved all the nature programmes in particular . . .

The dog was back on the wall again. But this dog wasn't Blaze. Funny how they all liked to lie there, and watch what went on around them when they weren't working.

This was Dart, a great-great-grandson of Blaze.

A whistle recalled the collie to its work, but it paused by Dan to greet him like all the dogs did.

Three bonny litters Blaze had given him. He could see the pups now, first so tiny and then later, stumbling and rolling over one another.

His elder son bred sheepdogs, too, and the litters tumbled at his feet so that he could watch them, gaining endless pleasure from the tiny animals, so self important, exploring this wonderful new world where so much happened.

He glanced at the wall again, and was sure that Blaze was back, watching him, waiting for him . . .

★★★★

Tai, the Siamese, appeared, walking regally, her black tail held high. She gazed up at him, blue eyes in a black face, black paws like stockings on her creamy body, and, with a little mew of delight, jumped on to his lap.

She looked up again and patted his cheek, then cuddled down with a deep sigh of contentment.

"Fancy a little more daylight, Dan?" Jack said, arriving like a genie.

He had brought another hot water bottle that he tucked into the back of the wheelchair, and another blanket.

"You hate coming in, don't you? Plenty to look at here for a little while yet. Can you see that kestrel, high in the sky?"

The hand tapped "yes". Dan had been watching it. Lucky bird to fly free.

The cat on his lap lifted its face and triggered yet another memory.

Alice had bred so many, and his daughter-in-law bred them now, carrying on her line. This was the image of Misty.

Misty! His busy mind flicked back to the past. To their trip to Paris, the only time they had ever been abroad.

The boys had given them their tickets and the hotel reservation as their silver wedding present.

Everything was already paid and they were booked into the bridal suite.

"You earned it," they said,

That long weekend in Paris had been their first holiday for years. No farmer could leave his animals for long. They needed tending night and day, seven days a week. It was a hard life, but he wouldn't have had any other.

He and Alice had been like two children, set free from school.

They'd sat outside the little cafés, watching the world go by.

He had bought her a frivolous, lacy negligee, not suitable at all for a woman her age, she said, but she loved it all the same, and wore it often. She had never had anything like it.

In return she had bought him the watch that he still wore. One day it would be Charlie's . . .

It was like the honeymoon they'd never had. And though neither of them were as young as they'd been as newly-weds, their love was deep and rich and fulfilling.

And Alice, such a bonny woman, a good wife, too — a wife to treasure.

He'd tried to show her how much he cared, for there had never been flowery words between them. Yet he was sure she'd known the depth of his love.

And she'd be waiting for him, he knew . . . out there.

Misty had been so excited to see them on their return that she had whirled round the house, tapping at everything that came her way.

She played with her paper ball, tapped at the acorn on the bathroom light cord, and when they went to bed, she still carried on dancing by herself, overjoyed to see them and unable to express her pleasure in any other way.

He never looked at her again without being reminded of a cancan dancer . . . and their glorious holiday in Paris . . .

DARKNESS was coming in surprisingly early, he noted. Blaze was back, lying on the wall, looking at him, appearing so real that he felt he could touch her.

He whistled, and surprised himself when the sound came out strong and true and the dog leaped down and ran to him, her hard little body pushing against him, jumping up at him eagerly.

"Did your mistress send you to say that my supper was ready?" he asked her and she barked at him, her head on one side, eyes alight with eager life.

He swung himself out of the chair, and strode after her, along a pathway that led from the darkness to a water meadow blazing with light.

At the far end was the farmhouse, out of place and out of time, smothered in a foam of roses, though roses were no longer on the wall of his old home. They had been cut down years ago.

Alice stood in the doorway, her dark curls tumbling around her shoulders, smiling at him, and he was young and strong again and the dog was running round him, darting away, then back again, greeting him as if they had been apart for years — as indeed they had — but he had forgotten that.

He put an arm round his wife, and walked into the farmhouse with her. He could smell roast beef cooking, bread baking and on every shelf he saw jars of marmalade.

"Welcome home," she said, and closed the door behind him.

★★★★

"Poor old boy," Jack said regretfully when he went to bring the old man in. Immediately, he rang Dan's sons to tell them that their father had slipped away during the afternoon, dying peacefully in his chair, with such a wonderfully happy smile on his lips.

Oddly, Jack had thought that young Dart had been lying on the wall when he came out, but he must have been mistaken, because when he turned his head there was nothing there, only the flowers and the leaves and the old man's crook, as if he had gone indoors, forgetting it.

Perhaps the little lass had brought it out to play with. It had certainly never been there before . . . ■

The Gifts

Of The Season

by Elizabeth Farrant

Now, in the autumn of her years, she
discovered feelings she thought had passed
her by for ever . . .

MISS PARTRIDGE opened the window of her neat little bed-sit. Yes, there was a decided nip in the air . . . She glanced at her watch. Five minutes to go before it was time for her to set out for the office. Checking the contents of her uncluttered handbag — glasses, loose change for the bus, clean white handkerchief (she'd never got around to using tissues) — she reminded herself that this was September, less than a month till her birthday.

As a child, she had always thought she was lucky to have a birthday in October. It was her favourite month — the sunshine, mellow and never too oppressive, the old-fashioned garden at the back of the cottage, which had been her home, a glorious tangle of asters, Michaelmas daisies, dahlias and chrysanthemums.

With the rest of the family, she'd gathered great glowing armfuls for the harvest festival at the village church every year.

She sighed as she pulled on her gloves. When you were young, there was always such a lot to look forward to. It occurred to Miss Partridge that there was not so very much these days.

Ah well, she mused, self-pity never did anyone any good. A few busy hours at the office would certainly put a stop to all this nonsense.

THAT MORNING, ashamed of giving way to such gloomy thoughts, Miss Partridge worked even more conscientiously than usual, and by lunchtime she felt much in need of her usual solitary snack at the Kosy Kafé, just a few streets away.

Arriving early, she found herself a corner table, but while she was studying the menu, she was aware the little room was filling up quite quickly.

"Excuse me, but is this place being saved for anyone?"

Miss Partridge looked up, startled. The man who was standing opposite was neither tall nor handsome and there was more than a hint of grey in his hair. His smile was shy and hesitant, but his eyes were kind.

"Oh, no," she assured him quickly.

They didn't talk much, Miss Partridge and the stranger who shared her table, just little snippets of conversation.

"Cooler today, don't you think?"

"Yes — quite a nip in the air."

"I like this little café — funny I've never discovered it before. Much better than those noisy, self-service places."

"Oh, yes — much pleasanter."

When they had finished their coffee and Miss Partridge got up to go, the stranger smiled at her — a little less shyly, now.

"Perhaps we'll be meeting here again?"

She nodded, smiling back, though secretly she told herself that this was most unlikely.

But the very next day they again shared a table at the Kosy Kafé, and again the day after that, till the midday meeting became a pleasant habit — an occasion to look forward to.

They still talked very little about themselves, but each seemed to sense that the other was lonely, and their loneliness became a bond between them.

From significant little things about his appearance — a slightly frayed cuff, an occasional button missing from his shirt, the lost look she sometimes noticed in his eyes — Miss Partridge deduced that her companion didn't have a wife.

Soon he took to walking her back to the office after lunch, which caused an amused ripple of excitement in the typing pool.

"Quite a dark horse, aren't you, Miss Partridge?" giggled Louise, the cheeky junior. "About your boyfriend, I mean."

Miss Partridge glared at her icily. The remark was as stupid as it was impertinent.

Boyfriend indeed! What an expression — and quite uncalled for, too! Why, they hadn't even told each other their names. In fact, the only remotely personal details they had exchanged were their star signs when he read her horoscope from the day's paper!

But as if he'd read her mind, her new friend put that right on their very next meeting.

"It's time we introduced ourselves," he said. "My name's Bradshaw. Norman Bradshaw."

"Mine's Partridge . . . Frances . . ." she tailed off. Never, she thought, had her own name sounded quite so ridiculous. But Norman Bradshaw didn't laugh at it.

"Frances," he repeated thoughtfully. "Frances . . . yes, I like that — it's a beautiful name."

THAT evening, Miss Partridge made a startling decision. Tomorrow she would wear her new blue dress — the one she'd bought to keep for special occasions.

After all, she argued with herself, this was a special occasion. She had ceased to be dull, plain, efficient Miss Partridge. She was Frances — a woman with a beautiful name . . .

Sitting at the usual table at the Kosy Kafé, feeling curiously young again and aware that the dress was decidedly becoming, Miss Partridge watched the doorway for Norman Bradshaw.

Next day would be her birthday — her 60th. It was years since she'd wanted to say to anyone, "It's my birthday tomorrow," but suddenly she found herself thinking that she would rather like to tell Norman Bradshaw about it.

Though, of course, it wouldn't do. He might — appalling thought! — jump to the conclusion that she was angling for a present.

But as soon as she saw him, she was conscious that today he was different — as polite as always, but sort of remote and distracted.

All through the meal he was silent and preoccupied. Then, when it was almost time to go, he asked her with a sudden startling abruptness, "Which, in your own opinion, are the prettiest flowers?"

This was a subject close to Miss Partridge's heart. Her eyes lit up as she responded eagerly, "The autumn flowers are far and away my favourite ones of all."

And she began to describe them to him: the purple asters, the deep blue Michaelmas daisies, the yellow chrysanthemums — all the familiar flowers which had helped to make up the magic of those autumns years ago.

Norman leaned forward confidentially. "I'm really grateful for your help," he told her. "You see, a very special friend of mine is having a birthday quite soon . . .

"Well, actually, she's more than a special friend. I want to marry her — if she'll have me, that is." His smile was almost boyish.

"I've never been much of a one for pretty speeches, so it seemed like a good idea to say it with flowers. And you're the only person I felt I could turn to for the advice I need."

Miss Partridge felt her smile freeze on her lips. The light died out of her eyes as all the silly, romantic notions of the past few weeks were shattered completely in a single moment.

She heard herself answer him coolly, composedly, in a voice which somehow didn't sound like hers. "Forgive me, I didn't understand at first — the flowers I mentioned were just my own personal favourites.

"The kind of bouquet you'll need for this special occasion can be made up by any reliable florist — I would suggest The Flower Pot at the corner."

She glanced at her watch. "Goodness, is that the time? Excuse me, I must fly."

Then, briskly, she gathered up her gloves and handbag and hurried through the doorway, not giving Norman Bradshaw a backward glance.

Somehow she managed to struggle through the rest of the day

without once betraying her bitter disappointment. But at night, her defences down, she lay awake for hours, re-living over and over in her mind that scene in the Kosy Kafé, blaming herself for having been so foolish as to take for granted that Norman, like herself, was unattached.

And as the first frost of the autumn silvered the pavements outside, Miss Partridge's tears fell, unnoticed by the world, into her pillow . . .

AS a result of her bad night, she overslept, and on her birthday morning the reliable, efficient Miss Partridge arrived ten minutes late at the office for the first time in twenty years.

She was met by Louise.

"Oh, there you are, Miss Partridge! Thank goodness you've come. Look, these were left for you in reception first thing this morning — by you-know-who!

"He made sure he'd got the date all right. Stopped me outside the office days ago and gave me no peace till I told him . . .

"So there you go. Happy birthday!"

And into the arms of the astonished Miss Partridge she thrust an enormous lop-sided bunch of autumn flowers. There were purple asters and deep blue Michaelmas daisies, scarlet dahlias and brilliant yellow chrysanthemums.

The note attached was as simple as it was brief. *To Frances, with love and best wishes for a happy birthday, from Norman . . .*

The eyes of the whole office were watching her and, as she bent over her giant bouquet, touching the flowers gently one by one, the girls drew close together and whispered to each other.

But Miss Partridge neither knew nor cared what they were saying. She opened the window and looked out into the mellow autumn light, where the sun had broken through the early morning veil of mist.

It was beautiful, and Miss Partridge glowed at the thought of the strange new happiness which was coming into her life.

And she smiled a little secret smile to herself and told herself once again how lucky she was to have a birthday in October . . .■

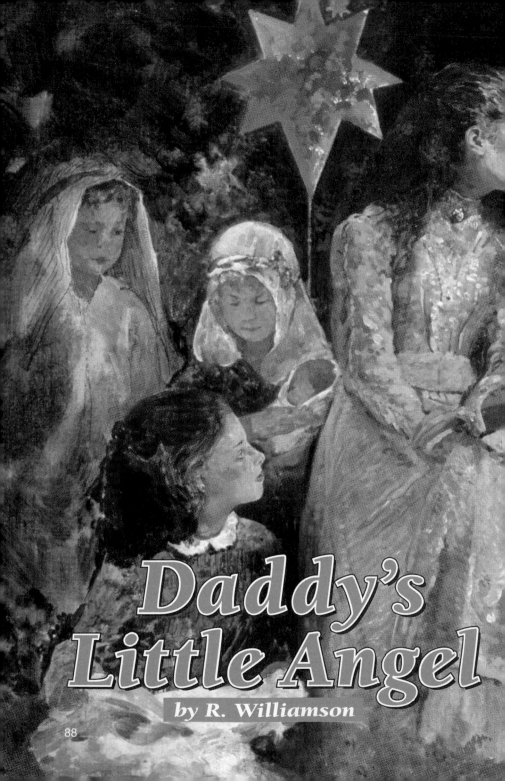

Daddy's Little Angel

by R. Williamson

He'd made the wings for his daughter's Nativity costume — and learned to spread his own a little . . .

GEORGE KNIGHT was a sucker for damsels in distress, which, in the overall scheme of things, was fine, because he was rather good at it.

Changing tyres, stopping leaks, wiring plugs, patching grazes, mopping-up spills and mending dolls were all grist to his gallant mill.

The last three skills were vital and much-used talents, since George's chief damsel-in-distress was Robyn, his seven-year-old daughter. She was in distress now.

"I won't go back!"

"Darling, you have to."

"I won't! I won't! I don't like it there now."

"You liked school last week, pet. What's wrong with it now?"

With just three weeks left before the end of term, with the whole curriculum given over to making sticky greetings cards and wonky-legged reindeer, how could anyone not like school?

In fact, given the offer, George would have swapped places with his daughter in a trice!

Mind you, not that his work was so terrible these days — not since he had hired Victoria to help. He could never have imagined, when he interviewed the petite, auburn-haired tornado for the job, that she would prove to be so invaluable.

Victoria was an absolute godsend, whose only fault, if it was a fault, was to lecture him on his private life. The crux of her argument seemed to revolve around the fact that George didn't actually have a private life.

George had a wonderful daughter and, in spite of what Victoria and his mother kept saying, that was enough for him. Robyn needed him. Needed him right now, in fact.

"I don't like my teacher."

"Yes you do. You like Miss White. You think she's wonderful. What's wrong with her all of a sudden?"

"She's an old witch! She's dead mean and horrid and . . ."

Words failed Robyn and she looked up at her father with such an expression of outrage that George felt his resolve begin to crumble, as it always did whenever his daughter looked at him like that with her dark, melted-chocolate eyes.

She wasn't playing fair.

FOR a brief moment, he wondered how Patty would have managed this little scenario. But it had been four long years since his wife had died and George had learned to cope with Robyn on his own.

"A witch, sweetheart. Are you sure?"

"Yes! A mean, old, sour-faced witch!"

"You mean she has a black cat, and a broomstick and turns people into frogs?" George sounded suitably horrified.

Robyn giggled. "No, Daddy. But she's horrid. She has beady eyes and her hair's all white and she scrapes it back like this." Robyn tugged her blonde hair back into a pony-tail.

"Well, she certainly sounds horrid all right," George agreed.

But in his mind he held a picture of the real Miss White.

Viking blonde, with skin like alabaster and clear blue eyes. She was a real head-turner and an angel with the kids.

"But that's no reason not to go to school."

Robyn's smile of triumph faded swiftly and her chin slumped to her chest until it was lifted by her father's finger. He stared into the deep brown eyes that were a painful daily reminder of his wife.

"What did she do, princess? Did she tell you off?"

A guilty flush stole up her cheeks. "Yes, but it wasn't all my fault . . . well, not really. And now she won't let Caroline sit next to me any more!"

Ah, the truth at last! Caroline was Robyn's next-door neighbour, friend and constant companion.

"Perhaps if I spoke to Miss White?" he suggested.

"OK." Robyn's response was limited and George realised something bigger was afoot.

"What else, poppet? What else is wrong?"

He was surprised and horrified to see tears well up and tip over her lashes. " And now I can't be in the Christmas play."

The full scale of the tragedy was brought home and George mentally revisited his plan for the rest of the week. Tomorrow he was too busy, but the day after he would go to see Miss White.

It would be difficult getting away from the office early, but Victoria would cover for him while he did the big tough father bit.

BY the following evening, however, Robyn had swapped one crisis for another. As George explained that he hadn't had time to see Miss White today, but he would definitely pop in tomorrow to sort out the Caroline situation, Robyn lifted a tired little face to his.

"Oh, that's OK, Daddy, Caroline and I can sit together again."

"Oh, that's good." Something was clearly still wrong, though. Instead of her usual bubbly self, Robyn sat in a lack-lustre heap on his lap.

"So what's the matter now, poppet?"

A heavy sigh greeted him. "I've got to be an angel."

"But that's good, isn't it? Yesterday you couldn't be in the Christmas play at all, now you've got a part. That's great!"

"But I haven't got any words, Daddy. I just stand there. The boys get to be sheep and cows. I have to be a rotten old angel in a stupid white dress!" She waved a note at her father.

George read it and swallowed. Suddenly the full scale of the disaster was horribly apparent.

To encourage parent participation at this very special time of year, the letter said, parents were being asked to make the costumes.

George stared at the little sketch enclosed with the letter and quaked. It was a long, white, floaty dress.

GEORGE was still depressed at work the following morning. Even the overnight transformations of the normally drab office into a glittering Santa's grotto did nothing to cheer him.

Victoria strolled into his office at ten, balancing two coffees and a couple of jam-filled croissants on a tray. George did manage to perk up a little at the sight of the pastries.

Victoria misread his glum face. "You're upset about the decorations, right?"

"No," George mumbled through a mouthful of crumbs. "I like it. I never thought of decorating the office before."

A lot had changed since Victoria had come to work for him: efficiency — up; morale — up; decorations — up. It seemed a natural progression, really.

"So, what's the beef then, boss?"

"This." George handed over the note from the teacher and the much-thumbed picture of the angel costume. He was surprised to see enthusiasm spark in Victoria's eyes.

Her face lit up with a smile and, for a moment, George was dazzled.

She was so pretty — her dark red hair seemed perfect against the holly-coloured wool of her sweater.

"So Robyn's in the Nativity play? That's fantastic!"

"No it isn't," George said dully. "I've got to make her an angel's frock."

"You can do it, George. All you've got to do is join two bits of cloth with a needle and thread. No problem for a whiz with his hands like you."

George stared at his hands. He hadn't thought of it in those terms.

Was it really just DIY with cloth instead of wood? He perked up instantly. "Right then, I'll give it a try!"

Victoria's smile of approval was reward enough.

The following morning, George's despair was as great as ever. He explained his failure.

"I got Patty's sewing machine out of the loft."

Victoria winced, as always, at the mention of his dead wife. It made her feel so guilty for liking George so much.

He sighed. "I don't know, I can fix my car in ten minutes flat, but I couldn't manage that fiddly, fan-dangled machine!"

Victoria smiled at him. "Would you like me to help?"

"Would you?" George clutched at the offer like a drowning man at a life-belt. "Tell you what, come back this evening. We'll make a start."

SO, at five-thirty that evening, George rang the doorbell of Caroline's house, where Robyn spent the time between the end of school and her father's return from work.

George and Victoria huddled on the doorstep, stamping their feet against the numbing cold air that promised snow.

George smiled involuntarily as he heard Robyn's approach, but instead of rushing into her father's arms as she always did, Robyn stood stock still halfway down the hall.

She stared at the person beside her father, outrage in every line of her body.

George was confused, but Victoria recognised the signals coming off the little girl: another woman was on her patch!

"You've got a red nose," Robyn declared rudely.

"I've also got some humbugs." Victoria smiled, unruffled. "Would you like one?"

A truce was declared for as long as it took the minty sweet to reach the relative safety of Robyn's mouth. They waited in silence while George unlocked the front door.

"Why are you here?"

Roughly translated, Victoria knew this to mean, "Why don't you go home?"

"I've come to help your daddy make your costume for the Nativity play."

A brief widening of childish eyes showed some surprise, but no real enthusiasm. Victoria's heart ached for George, who didn't completely understand what was going on.

As she wrestled with the recalcitrant sewing machine, Victoria tried again.

"You know, you're so lucky to be an angel," she said, as Robyn's tight little face peeped over the edge of the table.

"You think so?"

"Oh, I do . . . You're God's messenger. You speak to Mary and Joseph, the shepherds and the three kings. Then you stand guard over baby Jesus while He sleeps.

"I think you've got the most important part in the whole play!"

Robyn was almost, just almost, convinced.

"I have to hold a harp!" There was disgust in her tone.

"Oh dear." Victoria sounded suitably upset and, feeling she had found an understanding soul-mate, Robyn confided her deepest hurt.

"I wanted to be a sheep."

"I wanted to be a star."

As she said this, Victoria found both Robyn and George staring at her in amazement. They were so alike: same honey-coloured hair, same soft smile, and Victoria's heart melted.

"When my school did the Nativity play, I wanted to be a star and fly over the stage on a wire."

"And did you?" Robyn asked quickly.

"No, I had to be in the choir instead. I just wore my boring old school uniform and waved a tambourine and sang."

Robyn looked shocked and Victoria knew a truce had been achieved.

★★★★

When Victoria had finished at the sewing machine, she made Robyn parade in her costume for her father's benefit.

"What do you think, Mr Knight?"

Mr Knight? George blinked. What had happened to his Christian name? Then he realised that Victoria was being tactful.

"It's . . ." He strove for a word to describe how perfect Robyn looked. But the defiant tilt of her little chin made words like "cute" and "pretty" inappropriate.

His mouth dried and Victoria came to his rescue.

"Of course," she said smoothly, "when you've made the wings, it'll look absolutely super. "Wings?" George queried weakly.

"Wings!" Victoria and Robyn confirmed as one.

★★★★

At work the following day, George was fulsome in his thanks to Victoria, but she shrugged them off.

"Nonsense, George. I did it because I wanted to. I like sewing. I also like Robyn. She's a great kid."

"You think so? I mean, you really think she's OK? I worry about her sometimes. You know, about her being brought up in a one-parent family.

"I wonder if it'd be better for her if she had a proper family."

"You are a proper family, George. Don't let anyone tell you different!"

94

"Yes, well, I like to think so, but I worry. I feel so bad when I let her down. Like this business with the angel's frock . . ."

"What nonsense!" Victoria snorted. "George, you dote on that child. She's wonderful. You've made an amazing job of raising her. So what if just this once you had to get some help? You can't do everything, you know. You're not perfect, George — you're not expected to be. You're just a daddy, not a superman for goodness' sake!"

The vehemence of her response stunned him. The trace of exasperation in her voice surprised him, too.

"I know that. This thing with the dress has made me realise that I can't do it all by myself. Maybe I should have someone to help me."

Victoria stared at her boss. Had he finally come to realise in his dear, sweet way that he needed a woman? But trust George to think of it because Robyn needed it, not because he needed it.

He'd be surprised to know how many women would be queuing up to help him once he said the word.

Would he realise, though, that she'd be up there at the front of the queue?

She adopted her forthright "nagging-for-your-own-good" voice to give her advice. It hurt less that way.

"Well, for goodness' sake, George, don't marry some poor woman just because you need a housekeeper! Or, if you do, don't you ever let her find out!"

And with that she left the office, leaving George staring after her, wondering at the bitterness of her tone. What had he said?

A FEW days later, Victoria arrived at the office to find a home-made invitation on her desk in Robyn's childish hand: *Please come to my play.*

She found George watching her reaction from the doorway. He spoke and there was an urgency in his voice that lifted her sagging spirits a little.

"Will you come? She really wants you to be there. She's dying to show you her wings."

Victoria stared at him, wondering if he would ever ask for anything for himself, wishing that he would. She just wanted him to open up the wall he'd built around himself and allow someone inside.

Someone, anyone . . . It didn't have to be her, not really, but a girl was allowed to dream, wasn't she?

"Of course I'll come," she said.

★★★★

Victoria was duly impressed with Robyn's wings. George had done a wonderful job on them and she leaned across to whisper this into his ear. George was powerfully conscious of her warmth at his side as they crouched in the too-small chairs crowded around the front of the tiny stage.

The Nativity play was, by its very nature, moving and funny by turns. Robyn stood centre stage, and George felt a rush of pride.

As the last note of the final carol faded into silence, the hall erupted into delight, heartfelt applause. George turned to his companion and was astonished to see the bright shine of tears in her eyes.

"Oh, wasn't it lovely?" Victoria uttered before sniffing into the shredded remains of a limp tissue. George could hardly believe his eyes.

In her nine months as his assistant, Victoria had shown herself to be a no-nonsense tower of strength. She was sensible, pragmatic, go-getting and funny.

But sentimental? He would never have dreamed it possible.

He stared at her in all her soft-hearted, red-nosed glory and smiled.

"Aren't you proud of her?" Victoria's expression was rapt. "She looked like an absolute angel."

George slipped a comforting arm around her shoulders and was surprised how good it felt. He was used to offering shoulders to lean on, but this was different.

Very different . . .

He helped her on with her coat and revelled in her femininity: the shine of her hair, the smoothness of her cheek, the way she moved.

"You know," he said thoughtfully, "I should be taking you out to celebrate. If you hadn't done such a good job on the dress, the whole play could have been a nightmare."

Victoria stared at him and smiled. "That would be nice. Where do you think Robyn would like to go?"

"I wasn't think of taking Robyn with us."

"Oh!" Victoria's breath left her in a sigh as she realised that at least one of her Christmas wishes might be coming true.

But she hardened her leaping heart against rushing her fences and said, "Oh, I think it would be cruel to leave her out.

George stared down at his pretty, caring colleague and smiled.

She was right, of course, but a long-forgotten side of him was stretching its wings. It wanted to be selfish, wanted to have Victoria all to himself. It prompted him now.

"OK, but we'll arrange something for just the two of us for another time, how about that?"

"I'd like that," she said with a radiant smile, and as George looked into her sparkling eyes, he realised how much he'd like it, too. ■

On Our Own

by Carol Wood

*Her old life was gone forever, but perhaps
with her baby's love she could start
building a new one . . .*

HELEN gazed into eyes that were her eyes. They opened sleepily, as blue as cornflowers in a summer field. "She's the prettiest little mite in the ward," Sister Robinson cooed in her warm voice, a voice Helen suspected she reserved for all single mothers, a voice of compassion tinged with genuine sympathy and that, as usual, was what hurt most.

Helen fed her pretty wrinkled bundle, laid her back in her hospital blankets and waited for the appearance of the first visitor.

The first visitor, male or female, would precipitate a thudding in her heart, a wave of unfocused expectation soon to dissipate into disappointment.

For she knew no visitor would ever be David . . .

"It was a million to one chance," her mum had sympathised so many times she was beginning to dread the phrase. Though well meant, the words cut through her heart like a dagger each time.

It was a million-to-one chance he should cross the road that Friday night to buy a bunch of flowers for his new wife; a million-to-one chance he should be knocked down.

At twenty-eight, David had left her, unaware he had bequeathed the world a treasure.

"She's a Louise, I think, or perhaps an Emma — or an Annabelle," Helen's mother murmured, her face white and drawn. It was the strain, Helen thought guiltily, of the baby and me. Poor Mum.

"You'll come home to us, won't you — so we can help? You will let us at least do that? Just for a month or so?"

Helen nodded, pushing down the lump in her throat, as she sat on the edge of her bed holding the little African violet plant her mother had brought for her. She touched the little purple flowers and stroked the velvet leaves.

"Just for a couple of weeks," Helen agreed. And, summoning all her willpower, tried to complete her thoughts verbally.

"Mum, I can't keep putting off going — going . . ." She couldn't say it. She just couldn't.

The small word "home" remained elusive. "I must go back," she substituted on a sigh.

"But to be on your own there in that flat . . ."

"I shan't be on my own. I'll have Rose."

"Rose!" Mum gasped, sidetracked. "I should have guessed. That's a lovely name. Rose — the princess of all flowers."

"David's favourite flower," Helen said bravely. There, she had begun. By sharing that memory, by speaking his name, she had cleared a hurdle she had set herself through the pregnancy.

The moment her daughter had yelled out lustily for the joy of life, Helen had cried, "Rose!" knowing no other name would suit their daughter better.

There were more hurdles ahead, she knew that. But already she'd survived all these months without him. For now she had to reassure Mum and Dad. Living with them since David's death had been difficult, awkward, no-one knowing what to say or do with themselves.

"You're not going through each day without managing at least one smile," Dad had warned her teasingly. And even though she'd cried doing it, she'd smiled just to please him.

They'd all cried, then smiled, then got on with their lives, somehow. But now, only 24 hours after the miracle of Rose's birth, somehow everything had changed.

"Dad's parking the car. He won't be a minute. Now where's the little bonnet I knitted for her . . .?"

"Mum!" Helen tried to calm her mother down, assure her everything was in hand. "Rose is dressed. She's fed. All I have to do is carry her."

"Sorry, sweetheart, I'm an old fusspot. You'll be pleased when you're . . ." the husky voice trailed away. Even her mum couldn't say the word.

Instead, adroitly, she substituted, "settled".

ROSE, in the end, was the one who settled first, despite the chaos going on all around her.

Her mother and grandmother wore anxious frowns all day and her grandfather stalked the house by night peering into her cot with bushy grey eyebrows meeting worriedly in the middle.

Through it all, the little girl gurgled and blew bubbles and went contentedly back to sleep, leaving the whole household confounded.

At the end of the two weeks, Helen agreed to stay on for another.

"Just until I know I can feed her myself or whether I'll have to transfer to the bottle," she told her mother.

By two months, Rose was happily feeding from the bottle, still gurgling blissfully from the cot in the house in town.

Helen looked out one day and the rain and mist of the last few weeks had gone. The sun peeped through and there were girls strolling by in brightly-coloured clothes, smiling cheerfully at their boyfriends.

Helen turned away from the window, feeling the perspiration spread across her forehead. She wished she hadn't looked.

It was safe in this house. It had become a haven of disposable nappies, knitting, and books on babies. And, best of all, Rose to be cuddled.

Her biggest challenge was turning on the television and seeing life . . . and love.

"Mum?" Helen found her doing the ironing.

"I'll do your blouse, Helen, for clinic tomorrow. Dad will give you a lift. I'll come, too, if you like —"

"Mum," Helen gently interrupted. "I have to go . . ." She tried to say the word — and failed. She took another breath. "I have to go . . . back."

"But, Helen, you can't!" Her mum almost dropped the iron.

"I must!" Helen persisted, sitting her mother down on the kitchen stool, determined that this time she'd listen.

Then she took her mother's hands in her own.

"I'm strong enough now. You and Dad have been . . . wonderful, so wonderful. And I love you both so much. But I have to start living again on my — on our own. I have to take that responsibility."

"But it's . . . it's so early!"

"It's long enough, Mum. I have to do this. For all our sakes."

"She's right, love," Dad said from the doorway, a red-cheeked Rose in his arms. "Or we'll grow too fond of this one."

Rose gurgled and Helen knew in her heart, though she was dreading every step, that it was right to go . . . to go . . .

But the word remained firmly locked away.

ROSE cried all through their first night in the flat. Helen had never been so terrified. "Hush, my darling. Please don't, sweetheart."

Rose bunched her tiny pink fists and glared at the world through those wet cornflower eyes.

"Ssh! Ssh!" Helen began to sing. "Rock-a-bye baby . . ." She sang until she was exhausted. Then, just as she was returning the baby to her warm cot, the blue jewels flashed open, the tiny mouth wrinkled and the most heartbreaking noise Helen had ever heard bellowed out. The procedure was repeated for the next few weeks.

One afternoon, she sat, exhausted, at the little table and in the unusual quiet, glanced around the flat.

She seemed to be seeing it for the first time. Hers and David's flat — more or less bought and paid for, with very little mortgage outstanding.

At twenty-six when they'd married, she'd had her own place and David hzis.

Working in the bank, they'd both had good jobs. Selling up and buying this flat was an achievement when neither had reached thirty . . .

Suddenly the tears fell.

As though a dam had burst, they cascaded down her cheeks and plopped noisily into her cold cup of tea. She wiped them away and kept wiping until it was dark outside and Rose had begun to scream.

She missed her mum and dad, their security, their warmth. But most of all, she missed . . .

Suddenly, Rose went quiet.

Helen fled into the small bedroom.

"Rose! Rose!" Her frantic cries woke up the infant, who had drifted off into sleep and the two of them stared at one another — one in utter relief, the other in anger that she had been woken up so rudely.

They ended up cuddling, Helen wrapping her arms tightly around her treasure.

IN the morning, sunshine filtered through the flat. Helen heard a knock at the door and quickly went to answer it, thinking Dad had called round early with the papers.

It wasn't Dad, though, but a brown-haired man with spectacles and a suitcase in each hand. He looked bewildered.

"I'm, er, I'm awfully sorry to disturb you . . . but I'm Mike Taylor — your new neighbour?" She smiled. The flat upstairs had been on the market a long, long time. Almost since . . .

She had wondered who would buy it. He looked nice enough, a quiet sort, with dark brown eyes behind those funny spectacles. And then the thought struck!

He probably was a quiet individual, but was she? And, right on cue, a wail like a demented banshee pierced the calm morning air.

"Er . . . my daughter, Rose," Helen apologised.

Mike Taylor raised appreciative eyebrows. "What a nice welcome!"

They both smiled and Helen shook hands, trying to decide whether her new neighbour was exceptionally hard of hearing, or just a really good fibber.

★★★★

Mike Taylor never once complained about being woken up by the dreadful racket which filled the ground floor flat. He often knocked on Helen's door and offered to fetch her shopping on his way back from work, tactfully omitting to mention that his sleep had almost certainly been disturbed.

He mended things like plugs and drainpipes and chewed the fat with Helen's father over faulty central heating thermostats and a horrible crack in the bedroom wall which everyone reckoned was subsidence.

"He's a surveyor. He's going to ask a friend to come and do the repairs for you, or so Dad says," Mum told Helen one day as she strapped Rose into her high chair and began feeding her.

"He's about thirty-five-ish, wouldn't you say? Apparently his wife was killed a few years back. A plane crash; by all accounts. He's never mentioned it to me, but you know your father . . . they get on well together. But then Mike's so polite, so capable —"

"Mum!" Helen interrupted, suddenly feeling an odd sense of disloyalty and frustration. "Don't try to match-make. I'm not interested and I'm sure he's not either. He's just a very kind person who's a good neighbour — and that's the way it's going to stay."

"Me? Match-make?" her mother cried, "I'm doing nothing of the kind."

The feeling of annoyance grew.

It was especially noticeable, Helen decided, when Mike held Rose for one reason or another.

He never minded if she pulled off his spectacles, tugged his hair or messed up his clothes. He simply laughed with the child, his large brown eyes warmly accepting everything his assailant meted out.

"You mustn't let her do that, Mike!" Helen said sharply one day, gabbing Rose out of his arms.

The anger suddenly exploded in a great tidal wave of emotion, making her cheeks flame.

She wasn't really angry with Mike, she realised. She was angry with herself. And it was all so simple to explain.

She was beginning to feel again — to feel emotions other than grief or loss. After all this time, it was frightening and strange.

"Your daughter's certainly full of life," Mike grinned and walked to the door. "She has good taste, too. I hate these specs. It's about time I got myself a new pair."

Rose screamed after him, forming words that were unintelligible, but which seemed to mean she entirely agreed.

When the door closed, Helen lowered the child into the playpen with a big sigh. How time had flown!

Rose was sitting up all by herself now and crawling. The child grimaced, running her podgy fingers over tired eyes.

When she blinked hard and threw her plastic cat over the top of the pen, Helen knew it was time for forty winks.

While Rose slept, Helen madly cleaned the flat, prepared the dinner and tried not to think. Something was happening in her life and she wasn't sure she liked it.

The world at her parents' had been safe. She'd managed to establish some sort of safety net back here at the flat, too, keeping memories at bay by simply concentrating on each day's survival.

But lately, once or twice, apart from feeling confused, she had felt happy, too. It was an emotion so long unfelt that experiencing it was a shock.

She chopped the vegetables quickly, vacuumed like a whirlwind, tied her hair into a ponytail and scrubbed the clean kitchen floor even cleaner.

And at the end of all that, as Rose awoke, Helen realised with another horrible, heart-sinking shock, that she was still feeling happy.

IT happened on a Saturday, at Rose's first birthday. The party was a great success. Granny and Grandad were there, and Julie and her little boy Mark — whom they had met at the clinic — and a neighbour from the flat above.

When all the balloons had been punctured, the presents anointed with orange juice and crisps, then put away, Mike arrived.

"Happy birthday, Rose!" he exclaimed, producing a gift and giving it to her. With much relish, she tore it open to stare at the Sooty hand puppet.

"You put it on your hand like this," he demonstrated, catching hold of his own nose and tweaking it. Everyone exploded with laughter.

Helen found she was laughing, too, her blue eyes sparkling like her daughter's.

Guiltily, she stopped. Then Rose copied Mike's demonstration and Sooty pounced on Mike's nose, sweeping away his new spectacles.

In the midst of another burst of laughter, Helen caught herself, just fleetingly, thinking how attractive Mike Taylor was with those lovely brown eyes.

Afterwards, Mike offered to take Rose down to the shops in her pushchair while the clearing-up got underway. Granny and Grandad helped, then kissed her goodbye, exhausted from their day.

When she was alone, Helen stared out of the window, feeling both happy and sad at the same time.

Suddenly, a tall, brown-haired figure came into view pushing a pushchair with a sleeping child in it, and she seemed to hear a faint voice somewhere whispering, *"Be happy, Helen. Be happy . . ."*

Mike looked worried when he saw her pale face, but didn't say anything. Instead, he allowed her to help him manoeuvre the pushchair gently over the threshold in order not to wake the child and they stood, suddenly trapped by the unreal silence.

Hesitantly, Mike reached out and took Helen's hand in his.

"Today has been very special for me," he said softly. "I don't know if you can understand this, but walking back here with Rose, I felt for the first time in a long while, that I really wanted to come . . . home."

Helen nodded. She understood completely.

Home was the word she had been so afraid to use in case it didn't mean anything any more.

"Yes," she whispered, "it's good to be home." ■

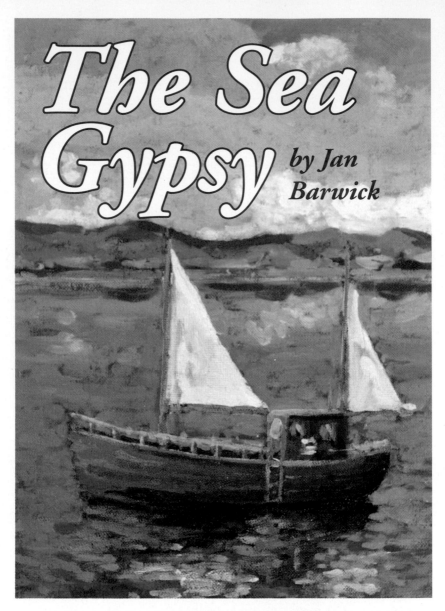

The Sea Gypsy

by Jan Barwick

Our love had sparked, flared and disappeared. But I knew now that it had never truly died . . .

SALLY'S day started innocently enough. "Come and watch the sunrise," she called upstairs to Ben. "It's a beautiful day." In the manner of teenage boys, however, Ben simply grunted and pulled the duvet over his head, so Sally went alone to the window of the living-room to admire the polished disc of the early sun creeping above the hill opposite.

Her gaze strayed down to the line of boats moored in the bay.

It was only an idle glance, yet in that second her well-ordered life was transformed.

Her hands trembling, she fetched the binoculars.

The image swam in and out of focus, but it was quite definitely Fly bobbing on the closest mooring.

An unusual boat — wooden, gaff-rigged, with white sails, now neatly furled — Griff had carved his own figure-head and fitted it beneath the bowsprit.

Sally roved the binoculars over the boat, then stopped sharply, detecting a movement in the cockpit.

A man emerged, a large figure, with thick raven hair and a black beard. Sally felt her throat go dry.

Fifteen years, and he had come back.

Sally closed her eyes, wondering at how the images of the last few minutes had instantly wiped out all the carefully buried control of a decade and a half.

Then she took several deep breaths to calm herself down and vowed that she would continue through the day as though the discovery had never been made.

Fate, however, had other plans.

MIDWAY through the morning, Sally had a phone call from Fred Lester, a guest of many years standing, an old faithful who regularly took a spring break at her little guest house.

Could he have a room for three or four nights? Sally assured him that he could.

And would it be possible for her to pander to his usual desire for fresh Dover sole?

Fred swore that no-one in the country could match the way she cooked it. Not to get it for him was as unthinkable as not being able to provide him with his special room. Laughing, she agreed.

The request, however, meant a trip down to the harbour where the fishermen held a stall three days a week.

And it was while she was waiting by the stall that Fate intervened.

The £20 note that she was offering in payment was suddenly snatched from her hand by a playful breeze and whirled up in the air, out and over the harbour wall.

Sally gave a squeak of dismay. The stall-holder, showing impressive agility for his age, leapt over his fish boxes and dashed to the top of the harbour steps.

Sally couldn't see above the heads of the crowd around the stall, and was still struggling with the incompletely wrapped bundle of fish.

All she heard was the stallholder shouting to a passing rower in a dinghy to fish the note out of the water.

"He's got it!" he shouted eventually.

Moments later the rower clambered up the harbour steps with his prize and handed it to the stall-holder.

The breeze rose again, tugging at Sally's newspaper-wrapped bundle. A sheet flapped and threatened to blow away.

"Oh, drat this!" she exclaimed, clutching at fish and paper in turn.

"Allow me," the rower said, coming to her rescue a second time. In a trice the bundle was secured.

"Thank you," Sally said breathlessly, and for the first time she looked up.

The blood drained from her face.

"Griff!" she said, her voice just a dry whisper.

A smile spread slowly across his face. "Great fires from Heaven," he said. "It's my own dear Sally."

He gave a great shout of laughter, and, oblivious to the amusement of the crowd still around them, swept her up in a breath-stopping hug.

Moons and stars swam before her eyes as she smelt his warm body smell, tasted the tang of salt in his hair.

The years ran away like sand through her fingers and she was twenty-two again.

The world was a cabin twelve feet long and she was safe in the warm and possessive arms of this marine gypsy who still had the power to stir her as no-one else ever had.

Then the sensation of vertigo, of falling, ceased, and he swung her down and placed her gently on the ground before him.

"I must get my change," she said, her mind thick with confusion.

She turned away from him, and the stall-holder, grinning, handed her the money.

Griff took her arm.

"Where to?" he asked. "How about The Steam Packet for lunch?"

"They closed that over seven years ago!"

Griff's grin was rueful. "Oh, well, it is rather a long time since I was here."

SALLY allowed herself to be steered into a small café. Griff signalled to the waitress and ordered coffee and cream doughnuts. Inwardly Sally smiled. So, he hadn't forgotten that particular weakness of hers!

Now they were inside she could study him more carefully. He hadn't changed much.

His hair had a frosting of grey now, and there were deeper, more permanent lines etched into the skin around his eyes, but otherwise he had the same extraordinary physical presence.

"I can't believe it's really you," he said.

"Why not? It's not a very big town. It's not surprising you'd run into me if you came here."

"I suppose it never occurred to me that you'd still be living here after all these years."

He pushed some grains of sugar into a little pile and said, "How are your husband and son?"

"How did you know I was married?" she asked, surprised.

"I came back a couple of years after we . . . separated," he said. "They said you had married Peter Westlake and had a little boy. I didn't come back again after that."

"Ben's a teenager now," Sally said carefully. "And Peter and I were divorced two years ago."

She spoke without emotion. Her marriage had been shaky for some years and it had been a relief when it ended.

Small, slight, blond Peter had been completely different from the giant Griff. He'd tried his best to compensate for Griff's departure from her life, but in the end he'd been unable to give her more than a token happiness.

"I'm sorry," Griff said.

"Don't be," she replied. "We were both making each other thoroughly miserable, and it was affecting Ben badly."

"What about you then?" she asked.

He shrugged and smiled at her. "Things don't change too much. I spend a while here, a while there. But, unlike you, I never married."

"A completely mossless stone." Sally smiled. "How do you manage it?"

"Not difficult. No-one ever reached your standard of excellence!"

She looked up at him quickly, but couldn't detect beneath his bantering tone whether he was serious or not.

"Where are you off to next?" she asked, changing the subject.

He leaned back in his chair. "In the short term, the answer's 'nowhere'. I've applied for a job as shipwright up at Booker's Yard for the summer. If I get it, which seems likely, I shall stay here for a while and get a flat in town. I was happy here once, there's no reason I can't be again."

She looked at him in disbelief. In all the years she'd known him, he'd never wanted to stay anywhere for more than a few days at a time unless he had to.

He had lived on the boat since the age of seventeen. In their years together, it had been their floating home.

Her thoughts flew back to that time. Nineteen, she'd been, when he sailed into the harbour for the first time.

"So you might see me around." His voice snapped her sharply back into the present. "If you can stand it."

He reached out tentatively and put his hand on her arm.

Could she stand it? Would it just be reopening old wounds? Could it possibly work?

She clutched the thought close and they sat in silence for a while, digesting the possibilities.

What about all the reasons for their original separation?

She'd wanted a family, a base that didn't rock.

Their few long trips to distant places like Portugal and the Azores had been enough for her. They had given Griff a taste for more — in contrast they'd given her the taste for home.

When they had come back to England, she'd wanted marriage and commitment. He had wanted the South Seas.

When the arguments had changed to rows, she had moved off the boat, hoping that he'd realise she was serious about settling down.

She'd waited a month, then, one morning, she'd looked out of the window of the flat she was renting and Fly was no longer on her mooring.

So that had been that. He'd abandoned her, and life had never been the same again.

AT that moment the door burst open and a crowd of teenagers clattered in. One of them detached himself from the group.

"Hello, Mum." Ben bounced over in his noisy, ebullient way. "We're having lunch in town for Mike's birthday."

He smiled at Griff. "Er, this is Griff," Sally said.

Ben grinned and held out his hand. "Hi. Nice to meet you."

Griff stood up and shook the proffered hand.

"I think I prefer fish and chips," Mike, the birthday boy, interjected.

Ben rolled his eyes in mock despair.

After a hurried discussion, the boys piled out the door, and Ben, bidding a hasty goodbye, pushed after them.

In the silence that followed, Sally stared at the table, the cups, the remains of the doughnut, the sugar bowl, anything not to have to look Griff in the eye.

Once, he had given her a photo of himself in the school rugby team. That laughing image could so easily have been her son.

At last, when the tension between them was so tangible that the air almost hummed, Griff spoke.

"Why did you never let me know he was my son? He is, isn't he?"

Sally took a deep breath and exhaled it in a long shuddering sigh.

"Oh Griff, be reasonable. I didn't even know I was pregnant when you left. I had no way of contacting you". She looked at him, and was surprised to see that his eyes were glistening. When he spoke, there was a catch in his voice.

"It took me the trip across the Atlantic to realise what I'd lost. I'd have been back months sooner if Fly hadn't been dismasted in a storm. Then, when I did get back you were married. It should have been to me."

"I thought you'd gone for good," she said. "Peter offered me the way out of an impossible situation. He offered me security, a name for my child."

"Does Peter think Ben's his son?"

She sighed and shook her head. "No. He knew what he was taking on when he married me, all credit to him. He never once treated Ben as if he wasn't his. I suppose it was easier because we never had any children of our own. He and Ben are very close."

"And what does Ben know of all this?"

"Ben thinks Peter is his father. I never saw any reason to tell him otherwise." Sally leaned back in her chair and pushed the hair back from her face. "Oh, Griff. What a mess. I'm sorry. If I'd known what today was going to be like, I would never have got up."

Griff reached out and clutched her arm. "You did love me, didn't you? It was special, wasn't it?"

Suddenly she felt exhausted. It had all been so easy before; just her and Ben, happy enough in their own quiet way. She felt unable to cope with this sudden upheaval.

She pushed his hand away and stood up abruptly.

"Griff, I said I was sorry and I am. I should never have come in here with you. We should just have said hello and left it at that."

And before he could respond, she turned and pushed her way out of the café, blind to everything but the imperative of escape.

She ran all the way home, panting as she tore up the steep steps.

When the front door was safely shut behind her, the tears came.

She cried for all the years they had never had, for the years they would never have.

LATER, exhausted by the tears and the emotion, she wandered through into the living-room and stared out of the window.

Fly bobbed on her mooring and she stared down at the little boat, transported back into the past.

The knock at the door shattered her reflections. Heavens! It must be Fred Lester — and his room barely ready. But when she answered the door, it was Griff's enormous frame that filled the doorway.

She stared at him stupidly, unable to speak.

"I had to do a bit of detective work to find out where you lived, you silly girl," he said. "This fish needs a good home."

Griff held out the bundle. She took half a step towards him, then one back, then suddenly they were in each other's arms.

In the minutes that followed, the misery of those wasted years just fell away. She was helpless in his arms, safe and protected, and it all seemed so right.

"I can't believe this is true. All these years I've been searching. You will marry me, won't you? Ben can be best man if you like," he said.

Ben!

She put her hands up to her face and stepped back. "Griff. I can't do it! Can't you see? Ben thinks Peter is his father. I can hardly turn round and tell a fifteen-year-old boy that the man he thought was his father isn't, and that a complete stranger is!"

Griff stood silent for a moment, then said hopelessly, "Do you have to tell him?"

"I wouldn't need to tell him. It's so obvious. He's the spitting image of you."

Since Griff's departure, Ben had been her reason for being. She couldn't take her happiness at his expense.

She put out her hand and touched him softly on the arm.

"He's your son, too, Griff. We have to do what's best for him. Perhaps when he's grown up . . ."

She left the rest of the words unsaid.

Griff took her face in his hands, stared long into her eyes, as if storing away the image for the empty times to come, kissed her once, briefly, on the lips, and left.

HOW long was it that she sat there, staring out at the sea? She didn't know, but the sun had moved round over the hill behind the house before Ben burst in, accompanied by Fred Lester. She stood up, pushing aside her own feelings of misery. Ben lobbed his schoolbag into a corner.

"Hi, Mum," he called. "Fred's here. He's just been telling me I ought to be setting my sights on university, like his grandson."

"Hello, dear," Fred said. "How nice to see you again. Yes, I've just been telling Ben about my grandson. He hopes to be off to Swansea next October to do electronics. Just like Ben, he is."

"Don't rush him," Sally said. "There's plenty of time for those sorts of decisions. He's only halfway through his GCSE course."

"Don't you believe it," Fred replied. "One minute they're in nappies, the next they're parents themselves. You make the most of him, my dear. He'll be gone before you know it."

"Who was that nice bloke I saw you with at lunch-time?" Ben asked, changing the subject and grinning at her.

"Oh, an old friend from years back. He's only in port for today."

"Pity. I liked the look of him. It's time you got yourself a boyfriend, Mum, then I wouldn't feel so bad about leaving you alone at nights while I take Lucy Everett out."

He ducked as she picked up a dishcloth and threw it at him, and pranced off into his bedroom.

"Sit down, Fred, and I'll make you a cup of tea," Sally said, as the strains of pop music came out of Ben's bedroom. "I'm afraid I'm running a bit late."

As she started preparing the meal, the thoughts pounded round and round inside her head.

Were her reasons for rejecting Griff the right ones, or was it out of fear that the past would repeat itself?

To put it bluntly, was she using Ben as an excuse?

Pity, I liked the look of him, he'd said. Was this an indication of what his feelings could become? And how would it affect his feelings for Peter?

But people had to come to terms with changes in their lives, and maybe Ben wouldn't so much be losing Peter as gaining Griff.

Sally sighed. Fred was right. Ben would soon be leaving the nest and she would be the one left behind . . . alone. She had a life, too, didn't she?

Suddenly, with total conviction, she knew that this extraordinary day had offered her a chance of a special happiness, and she had refused it. Was it too late to change her mind?

She ran into the living-room and peered out the window. In the bay, Fly's jibsail was creeping up the mast.

"Sorry, Fred," she called, "I just have to nip out for a moment." And for the second time that day, she found herself running at top speed down towards the harbour.

When she reached the bay, Fly's jib was fully set and flapping and Griff was unfurling the mainsail.

She ran along the towpath until she was opposite the boat, and stood panting for breath.

"Griff," she yelled, but he didn't hear her.

"Griff!" She jumped up and down, waving her arms. Fly turned her nose into the wind as the mainsail inched to the top of the mast.

"Griff!" And then he turned and saw her, a pale shape against the darkness of the hill.

"Griff!" But her hands had fallen to her sides, because in one rapid movement he was down in the tender and unshipping the oars and pulling towards her.

Fly span on her mooring, sails all adrift, and it didn't matter.

It didn't matter at all, because at last, after fifteen years, they were both coming home . . . ■

MORNING
WALK

A poem by Joyce Stranger, inspired by an illustration by Mark Viney.

UP in the morning
Out in the sun,
Taking my year-old pup
for a run.
He sees a rabbit,
At once gives chase.
Bun dives down a hole
And that ends the race.
Wait! There's a hedgehog
Rooting in grass.
That's much too exciting
For pup to let pass.
Off like a rocket,
All he finds is a ball
Of spikes and of prickles
Which is no fun at all.
Pup runs back to
me, wailing,
He's learned a new
lesson.
Hedgehogs aren't
good to chase.
He's not anxious to roam,
So now our walk's ended
And we set off for home.
Away in the woods
The hedgehog freed
from his fright
Continues his feeding
Long into the night.

The Courting Hat

by **Marian Hipwell**

Was it just coincidence, or did
Grandmother's hat really have
"charming" powers?

FIRST saw the wretched thing in my grandmother's attic. "Ah!" Noting my interest, my grandmother picked up the green felt hat. "That was my courting hat, Julie."

"Your what?" I asked disbelievingly.

"You young ones are so cynical these days," she reproved. "You have no faith in the power of destiny."

I had. I just didn't see what that old hat had to do with it. In its day, it had probably been quite a head turner. Now, it was decidedly out of style, though the feather sticking out of it was still rather jaunty.

"All I'm saying is that the first time I wore it, a handsome young man I'd never spoken to before came up to me and admired it. That was your grandfather."

She turned the hat over in her hands, her expression dreamy. "'I say, that's a fetching little number.' Those were his exact words — I've never forgotten them." I eyed her affectionately. How simple she made it all sound! Unfortunately, in my experience, getting a man to notice you required a bit more subtlety than that. Not to mention perseverance.

I should know; I'd been trying to catch Rick Talbot's eye for months now. It was even out of a desire to please him that we were here at all, combing my grandmother's dusty old attic for jumble.

Since Rick — a teacher and old university friend of my brother, Ken — recently transferred to the area, he's forever needing stuff for this fête or that jumble sale. I live in hope that one day soon, he'll realise how much he needs me, too . . .

"You ought to try something like this!" Gran remarked now. "You're how old — twenty-seven? And still unmarried!

"Here . . ." She thrust the hat into my hands. "Try it. Go on — I dare you. There's no harm in trying the old ways, is there?"

There she went again, inferring that the hat had certain powers. And as for wearing it when Rick was around, I could just imagine his expression.

He'd notice me all right, but for all the wrong reasons!

I'd thought that was the last I'd see of the hat, but when I dumped the box of jumble on to the table in the parish hall that evening and started to empty it, the hat was the first thing I saw.

"Oh, how nice!" Pamela Baines, the leading light in the parish amateur dramatic society, had lingered after rehearsals. Crossing to my side, she picked the hat up and held it aloft admiringly.

"It's just what I've been looking for, in fact," she continued loudly. "We're doing a Noel Coward season, and this is far better than anything the wardrobe's come up with. Could I borrow it, please?"

"Be my guest," I said.

Perching the hat on her head, Pamela eyed herself in the mirror on the opposite wall.

Hearing a noise, I turned to see Rick and one or two other people entering the hall with piles of jumble. At the sight of Pamela in the hat, Rick halted.

"I say, that's a fetching little number!" he exclaimed. I looked at him sharply. Coincidence, it had to be.

"Julie says I can borrow it for the play," Pamela said.

"Oh, you're interested in amateur dramatics, are you?" Rick asked. "I've always fancied trying that myself." It was, I decided, time to let them both know I was here. Just in case they had forgotten.

"Oh Rick, this is Pamela Baines." "Pamela, Rick Talbot."

"Hi," she said.

"Hello." Rick's tone was unusually warm.

There was definitely magic in the air, but not where it ought to be.

★★★★

"Rick wondered if you'd like to go along to the last night of Pamela's play," my brother, Ken, said one evening.

"Really?" I asked, delighted. Perhaps I'd been a little hasty in my judgement of Gran's hat, after all.

"Yes. Pamela gave him half a dozen tickets," Ken told me. "She's invited him — all of us — to the party afterwards, too. Should be fun."

I sighed. Far from redeeming itself, that hat had a lot to answer for. I tried to look on the bright side. Rick wouldn't really want to spend the rest of his life kicking his heels in the third row front stalls, watching his beloved gazing deeply into the eyes of another man, would he?

It didn't seem to worry him on Saturday night, though. His expression lit up each time Pamela came on stage. And I wasn't really surprised to hear at the party later that he had enrolled as a member of the group.

"Hi! Did you enjoy the show?" I turned to find Pamela at my elbow.

"Very much," I said truthfully. It was the audience — at least the part which Rick constituted — which had me on edge.

"You've never been interested in amateur dramatics yourself?" she was asking now. "You'd be marvellous, you know. You have the expressive face needed for acting. I can tell everything that's going on in your mind."

If that was the case, I decided, the sooner I took my expressive face home before anyone saw the aching heart beneath, the better.

On the way out, catching sight of Gran's hat on a prop where Pamela had casually tossed it, I made a detour and kicked it into a corner, from whence, I hoped, it would never emerge again.

IT was some months before anyone saw the hat again. I'd reluctantly agreed to take my sister's two children to see the Christmas pantomime which the amateur dramatic society was putting on.

Ken had told me that Rick was playing the lead. I hadn't asked who was playing opposite him. I didn't want to know.

As the lights went down, I admitted to a certain amount of curiosity about Rick's performance. And it would be nice to see him again, even if it meant watching him gaze adoringly into Pamela's eyes.

It was a shock, therefore, to see the lead being played by a small, dark-haired girl. In fact, there was no sign of Pamela in the cast at all.

In this modern production, men were men and women were women. No shapely-thighed Robin Hood here; just Rick in all his macho splendour.

After my first startled glance, I could hardly take my eyes off him. Not because I was still in love with him, which I was. And because he was a particularly fine actor, which he wasn't. It was the fact that he was wearing Gran's hat! I would have recognised that jaunty little feather anywhere.

Afterwards, I took the children backstage. Rick was lingering by the door, still in costume.

"Hi, Julie! I thought that was you, out there." He looked delighted to see me. More delighted than he ought to have been, for a man who'd lost his heart to Pamela Baines.

"Hello, Rick. That was a great performance," I said.

"Nice of you to say so," he responded. "But I'll never make an actor. I took the rôle because they couldn't find anyone else who looked young enough. Once they have some new members, I'll retire gracefully."

"I thought Pamela would be playing the female lead," I ventured.

"Oh." His smile was wry. "She left us for a bigger society. She'll do well," he said. "She's ambitious and talented. Not very nice, though." There was a whole world of meaning, not to mention a bruised heart, in those few words.

"I've missed you being around," he went on, a little hesitantly.

"Really?" I stared at the hat. "By the way, that's a fetching little number," I said, unable to resist it.

"Isn't it?" Rick grinned. "I found it in the corner covered in dust and thought it was perfect for this outfit.

"I don't suppose you'd like to come to the last night party tonight?" he asked.

"I'd love to," I said. A warm feeling was stealing over me. At long last, I could feel magic in the air.

My grandmother would put it all down to that courting hat of hers — even if it was on the wrong head . . . ◼

Promises...

by Nicola Slade

*Years ago he had sworn never to leave her.
Would Hilary ever come to terms with the
loneliness now he was gone?*

HILARY GRANT was an angry woman. Oh, not on the outside, of course. The outside of Hilary Grant, the one that was on view to the world, showed a still pretty, well-preserved, elderly woman, with well-groomed silver hair, periwinkle blue eyes and a slender figure.

Hilary's daughters eyed her sidelong and whispered about her in relieved tones to each other.

"Mother's coping extraordinarily well, isn't she?" the elder suggested. "I was afraid she'd go to pieces when Dad died. After all, they'd been married more than fifty years. But, all in all, she's an absolute wonder."

"She certainly is," the younger daughter agreed. "I think perhaps she's being brave for us all, she knows how much we miss him, too."

They were glad for their mother, and even more grateful for themselves, that they didn't have to cope with any more than a manageable amount of grief.

What neither of them knew, was that beneath their mother's quiet, well-behaved exterior, raged a bitter, furious woman.

Even from the beginning, from almost the moment of Will Grant's death, anger had been Hilary's predominant emotion.

Oh, it had been temporarily hidden by shock and sorrow and then subdued by a complete numbing of all emotions, but when feeling surfaced once more, anger was there; a violent, lashing rage that startled her with its intensity.

Now, six months after Will's death, Hilary was still angry, hugging the fury to herself in a secret passion, feeding it daily as she thought of him constantly.

The actual moment of his death played and replayed in her mind in a vivid, tormenting stream of sorrow.

He'd been sitting there in his comfortable old armchair, watching a favourite comedy on television, a nightcap glass of whisky in his hand.

A good way to go, they had all told her and she had nodded, all the time screaming silently that they were fools, that there was no good way for him to go.

"I feel so odd, Hilly!" he had remarked, his voice astonished the whisky crashing to the floor as his hand reached out for hers. Then suddenly he was gone.

"Will!" she had cried in terror. "Will!"

Then, in desperation, "Will, don't do this to me, don't you dare leave me!"

It was after that that she donned the cloak of sweet, well-behaved Hilary Grant — that dependable old lady; sad of course, after all those years of happy marriage, but not an embarrassment to anyone with unseemly displays of grief.

When she was alone, she remembered . . . all the years, all the happiness, all the anger and the sorrows. But with others she was quite cheerful, taking an interest in their doings, apparently perfectly rational.

But I'm not rational, she thought to herself ruefully one summer evening, after six months of this double life. I'm not rational at all.

"Oh, Will!" she sighed. "Why did you have to do such a stupid thing? You promised me, all those years ago."

"Promise," she had teased. "Promise me that we'll die together, the same split second, the exact, precise same moment in time."

"I promise." He grinned, kissing her. "The very same minute."

But Will had broken his promise and that was why she was still so angry with him, so angry with the world, at the injustice of it all.

THEIR marriage had been like any other, she supposed, looking back on it. Fifty years of ups and downs, highs and lows, sparkle and dullness, laughter and tears.

But there had never been a moment when either of them had regretted a single day. Never a time when his key in the front door hadn't sent a tingle to her toes and a lift to her heart.

I suppose I got cocky, she mused to herself now, rather surprised at herself. Humility wasn't much in her line. Defiantly standing her ground was more her style.

"A stroppy little thing!" Will used to call her, pulling her down on to his knee for one of the passionate embraces that so amused their cynical children, who wrongly believed them to be too old for love . . . for life.

★★★★

That night, Hilary slept soundly for the first time since Will's death. She woke to a feeling of peace, refreshed and comforted. Stretching lazily, she tried to recall her dream. Will had been there, that went without saying, but he had been telling her something.

She screwed up her face, frowning with the effort of recapturing the happy dream with its fading message.

"You have to stop all this anger, Hilly," he had told her. "It's not what I wanted for you, you know that, and it's not doing you any good at all.

"You have to channel it, somehow, all that energy and adrenalin, before it eats you up."

"But I need to be angry!" she cried aloud, sitting up in bed. "It helps me get through the days. I need it, to help me fight!"

There was no answer, but all that day and throughout the next, Hilary pondered Will's words.

It might have been commonsense speaking to her, of course, she knew that, but it comforted her to think that Will was looking after her still.

IN her heart, Hilary knew he was right, knew that already her terrible rage was dissipating, had been gradually fading for weeks, even months.

But what am I going to put in its place, she asked herself, strolling home from church that evening. The service had been comforting and she'd agreed to help with the coffee mornings again, but that wouldn't be enough.

"Channel the anger." Will's words drifted into her mind once again.

"That's all very well, darling," she thought, "but I wish you'd be a bit more specific".

Perhaps not surprisingly, Will kept an enigmatic silence as she crossed over the road into the park.

Something cold and wet nudged her calf and she jumped and looked down. At her feet sat a small, scruffy mongrel, gazing pleadingly up at her, big sad eyes imploring her to be kind.

"Really, Will!" Hilary burst out laughing, her first completely whole-hearted peal of laughter in six months. "What a cliché! You don't seriously expect me to fall for that old chestnut, do you? The sweet little puppy-dog bringing comfort to the lonely old widow? Give me credit for some kind of intelligence!"

With a kind pat on the dog's head, she set off briskly across the park, conscious that the scruffy little dog was trotting purposefully along behind her, with a spring in its step, hoping for a hand out.

The dog sat purposefully beside her at the park gates, grinning up at her as she stared helplessly at it.

"I don't know what you think you're doing," she said to the animal. "There's no way you can come home with me. I don't want a dog. Now shoo! Go away . . . go home!"

As her resolution began to crumble, she heard a shrill whistle and the sound of running feet and a large young man in motorcycling leathers panted up to her.

He was sweating and looked extremely cross.

"I'm ever so sorry, Missus," he panted, grabbing the dog by its collar. "Has he been bothering you? He's terrible for trying to scrounge food off strangers."

Hilary made her way up the garden path, chuckling to herself as she remembered the boy's abject apology and the dog's shameless efforts to exploit its doggy cuteness.

WHEN Hilary got home, she found a leaflet stuffed through the letterbox about the local animal shelter, asking for contributions and volunteers to help with fund-raising and work at the centre.

"Will?" she queried aloud. "Is this what you mean by channelling my energy into something useful? It's a bit glib, isn't it — out of the blue, like that?

"First a stray dog to win my heart, then dozens of stray dogs needing help? But why animals? Why not some other charity work, involving humans?"

She pottered about the kitchen, whistling to herself, making a mushroom omelette and a small salad, laying a place at the table for the first time since she'd been alone.

Later, over a cup of tea in the lounge, she relaxed. The late June sunshine streaming through the open window fell on the leaflets from the animal shelter strewn on the coffee table before her and she picked them up to read again.

"Why animals, Will?" she repeated and the answer slid into her mind.

"Because you're still too thin-skinned at the moment to cope with other people's problems, Hilly. You concentrate on the animal shelter for now. They desperately need help and you know how much you love dogs."

She smiled mistily. It was true, she did love dogs, but Will had been allergic to animal hair so they had never been able to have one. Maybe she could give a home to an old and lonely dog now, a puppy would be too much work.

"Oh, all right, you win."

She smiled and went upstairs to bed.

★★★★

Before she turned out the light, Hilary gazed at the framed photograph of her and Will on their Golden Wedding Anniversary and gently stroked his cheek.

And that was when she realised that the anger had gone completely, gone for ever.

It had served its purpose and brought her out of the pit of despair, and though she was still left with a sense of sorrow, her love for Will was whole now, not distorted by her rage and fury at his loss.

Life would go on. She would follow Will in due course, but in the meantime, she would cease to rail against Fate and do what he had said — channel the anger and the energy into something worthwhile.

"But I still think it was a sneaky trick, Will Grant," she murmured indistinctly as she dropped off to sleep, "getting someone else to do your dirty work for you. And I tell you what, when I do get round to getting a dog, I'm going to call him Willy, just to annoy you!"

In her dream, Will was shaking his head in mock anger at the despised nickname. His mother had always used it to embarrass him.

But it was only a happy, pretence reproof and Hilary smiled as she slept, secure in the knowledge of their everlasting love. ∎

One Of The Family

by *Teresa Ashby*

All you'd ever wanted was to belong. Surely
my own daughter wasn't going to stand
in your way?

I CAN hardly believe it's you standing there, looking so tall and proud
in your suit. For a moment, tears threaten, but I fight them back. You
wouldn't want me to cry, not today of all days — although we've
shed many tears together, you and I.

You glance at me, catch my eye and smile; a special smile meant only for me. I manage a watery response and hope you don't realise how hard I'm fighting to control my emotions.

I hide what I'm feeling by having a last-minute fiddle with Amy's dress. It doesn't need any adjustments, but I need a few moments to get myself together.

I want to shout out, tell everyone all about you — the truth, the real truth — but it's something I keep to myself because it's in the past and it would do no-one any good to know.

You were nine when you came to me. Just nine years old and such a poor little ragamuffin that my heart went out to you. Your clothes were too small and threadbare and your hair was too long and had been badly cut, leaving it all kinds of odd lengths.

How well I remember the day that Jean brought you to me.

"I know you said you didn't want any more," she said. "But this one is special. His name is Lenny. He's nine years old and what he needs most of all right now is a close, loving family."

It seems odd now, looking back, how devastated I'd been when the doctor told Tom and me that we were unlikely ever to have children.

Something wrong, he said. One of those things. But it hasn't stopped us being parents, albeit temporary ones, to so many over the years.

And we've never forgotten a single one . . .

Then Amy came along. When the doctor told me I was pregnant, I laughed at him, thinking he must be mistaken.

But he wasn't. By some miracle we were blessed with our very own child and she was born with a ready-made family of children we had fostered — three older brothers and one sister.

It used to confuse her at times, the way the other children came and went. Some only stayed a few days while their parents were in hospital, others stayed years.

I didn't realise how much it was unsettling her until one day, when she was five years old, she tugged at my sleeve and asked, "Will I have to go away soon as well, Mummy?"

I tried to explain, but it's difficult to understand when you're only five years old.

At that time there were two teenage boys staying with us, both of them from broken homes, both waiting for that magical day when one of their "real" parents would come and get them.

It was heartbreaking. Both sets of parents had remarried, set up new homes and started new families. None of them wanted unwelcome reminders of their previous marriages.

So Tom and I loved them, tried to understand them and shared our home with them.

That's when I told Jean I wouldn't take in any more. I had Amy and

Josh and Phil and I didn't want to upset Amy any more.

But Jean brought you to me and I knew I couldn't turn you away . . .

You'd been the victim of neglect. You were under-nourished, your skin was deathly white from being kept inside all the time and, for a nine-year-old, your speech was deplorable.

No-one had ever taken the time to talk to you. At school, the other children ridiculed you and the teachers hadn't the time to give you the special attention you so badly needed.

When I told Tom what you'd been through, he went very quiet, and I noticed his fists were clenched at his sides.

"I'd like to get my hands on them," he said softly. "A child is such a precious gift. How can anyone . . .?"

"Shh." I hugged him. "He's with us now. We'll make up for the past."

Easier said than done. You and Amy hated each other on sight. To my horror, I heard her making fun of you for your hesitant speech and I caught you pushing her into the hedge in the back garden by way of retaliation.

I used to watch you playing out in the garden a lot. You were always building things, Lenny. I can remember that you built a little enclosure for the woodlice and a birdbath, too.

One female blackbird was so tame, you had her eating out of your hand.

After you'd been with us just two years, I still sometimes felt no closer to you than the day you arrived. We bought you toys, but you weren't interested. All you really wanted was love — and to belong.

While Amy adored — and was adored by — her older "brothers", you and she were more like a real brother and sister. Always fighting!

When Josh left to join the Royal Navy and Phil won a scholarship to college soon after, Amy was devastated.

"Everyone I ever loved has gone!" she complained. "But I hate him and he's always here!"

She pointed at you and I could see her words wounded you deeply. For a moment, I thought you wouldn't respond, then you started shouting back.

There was nothing wrong with your speech by then and you spelled out very clearly and very precisely what you thought of my daughter.

Selfish was one word I heard you use, another was spoiled. Amy's mouth dropped open and she gaped at you in surprise. No-one had ever spoken to her like that before.

She turned to me, expecting me to rush to her defence, but I didn't. This was one battle she was going to have to fight herself.

IT was a full six months later that the matter resurfaced. You were out in the garden, your friendly little blackbird perched on your shoulder, when I heard a window open upstairs and Amy's voice drifted down.

"Do you really think I'm selfish?" she asked you.

You turned, looked up and grinned, and something inside me just melted. It was the first time, the very first time, I had seen you smile so genuinely.

"Sometimes," you replied.

"Well, I hate you!" she snapped.

I tried to talk to her, but my daughter was one small bundle of indignation. I began to wonder if maybe you were right, if she had been spoiled and if she was perhaps a bit selfish — but Tom put me right on that score.

"Far from it," he said. "Ever since she was born, she's had to share us with other children, and let's face it, Sandie, some of them have needed a good deal of your time and attention, haven't they?

"No, Amy's not spoiled, but I do think she's crying out for attention."

Dear, wise Tom. It came as quite a shock to realise that while I'd been doing such a good job with other people's children, I'd failed to see a need in my own.

I resolved to change. By this time, Lenny, you had changed from a skinny little boy with a dirty face and scruffy hair, into quite a presentable young man. Calm and imperturbable, with lots of friends, you had a quiet inner strength I knew would last you a lifetime.

I first saw that strength one summer when you were about fourteen.

★★★★

You were in the garden with your little blackbird again and Amy ventured outside and stood by the house, gazing enviously at you.

She was eleven by now and was going through a plump and clumsy stage. Gappy teeth, frizzy hair, freckles — you name it, the poor child was coping with it.

It was only a stage, it would pass, but when you're eleven, you think it will last forever, and that's how it was for Amy.

"Hi, Amy," you said, without turning round.

"Hello," she muttered.

I stepped back from the kitchen window, not wanting to eavesdrop, but at the same time, aware that something special was about to happen and I didn't want to miss it.

"Can I hold her?" Amy asked you.

"It's up to her," you answered diplomatically. "If you're very quiet and still and patient, I expect she'll come to you."

Amy crept up ever so slowly and knelt down on the grass beside you, her eyes wide with wonder. She'd envied you your special friendship with the little bird and now you were about to share it.

The blackbird hopped tentatively on to Amy's hand and cocked its head cheekily on one side.

Amy's face lit up, and for a second or two, my plain, plump little ugly duckling actually looked beautiful.

You saw it, too, Lenny. Your face softened as you smiled at her and I realised how fond of her you really were — despite everything.

It was a start, but it wasn't the solution; far from it. When you both reached your teens, there were always girlfriends and boyfriends to be teased about.

When you were old enough to leave home, you said you'd like to stay with us. We were delighted, but Amy was furious and claimed that you'd only stayed to annoy her.

Then Tom died. I don't think I'd have got through those painful months if it hadn't been for you and Amy.

For the first time ever you worked together and looked after me for over six months. But I didn't feel that things were anything like normal, until you started quarrelling again.

YOUR real father turned up one day. He was a rough sort of character, who may once have been very good-looking, but had let himself go.

He'd read about you in the local paper, for you'd set up your own motorcycle repair business and were doing very well. A small legacy from Tom had helped you take that first step and you'd never looked back. You'd even taken on a partner, Mike, a nice young man with bright blue eyes and floppy hair.

But now this man had turned up after all these years, and I was so afraid he'd spoil things.

A muscle twitched in your cheek as he tried to ingratiate himself with you. You hadn't forgotten his treatment of you, not one bit of it.

Only I knew what you'd really suffered, for you'd told me when I came in to sit with you at night when you suffered terrible nightmares.

You hadn't had the nightmares for a long, long time, but you would never forget.

"Please . . ." You turned to me and I understood. You needed to be alone with this man who called himself your father.

I left the room and bumped into Amy in the hall.

"You haven't left him alone in there?" she gasped.

By now she was a far cry from the plain child she had once been. A striking young woman, time may have eased her looks, but it hadn't softened her temper at all.

"He's got to deal with this on his own," I said. "He's a man now, Amy."

She turned from me then and stormed into the living-room.

"Get out!" she said, eyes blazing at the stranger.

I rushed in behind her and tried to stop her, but she was furious, she wouldn't be silenced.

"Who the heck are you?" your father demanded.

"This is my sister," you said. "Only she's more than that. She's my best friend as well."

"Sister?" the man spluttered. 'You don't have any sisters."

"Oh, yes he does!" Amy said. "He's family, and we stick together."

"I think you'd better go," you said flatly. "And I don't want to see you here again."

Your father didn't say a word, just turned on his heels and left.

I saw him out, and when I came back to the living-room, Amy was in your arms, shaking and sobbing, and you holding her, stroking her hair.

"I was so scared," she whispered shakily.

"So was I," you admitted. "But don't worry, Amy. He can't hurt me any more."

★★★★

With a jolt, I come to my senses and I give Amy a quick hug and kiss.

There is so much I want to say to her, but there isn't time, so I hurry away.

There is a restlessness in the church, an occasional cough, a bored child's impatient cry.

The music starts. About time, too! I seem to have been waiting ages, yet only minutes have passed since I hurried to my seat.

Everyone stands up and turns and I glance at you, Lenny, but you are looking at Amy and can see nothing else.

And no wonder. She looks absolutely beautiful as she glides down the aisle, a vision of loveliness in ivory satin. A veil hides her face but I can tell she is smiling.

And you look so proud, Lenny, so very, very proud. Mike is nervous. I expect he wishes you could have been at his side as best man, but you have a more important duty to perform.

You'd looked so happy when Amy asked you, but with a teasing glint in your eye, you'd said, "Give you away? Why, Amy, I'll pay poor old Mike to take you off our hands!"

And standing beside me in the charged stillness of the church as we wait for the service to begin, stands a quiet, shy girl.

Your girl, Lenny, the one you'll marry one day soon.

I sigh and wipe away a tear. My family keeps on growing . . . and it's wonderful. ∎

Love Thy Neighbour

by Cheryl Morgan

She'd tried everything to be friends with old Mr Grimshaw. But all he did was complain . . .

I CAN'T help feeling you bring these things on yourself, love," her mother said, when Shirley tried to explain why it had taken her so long to get to the phone, and why she couldn't stop and chat.

Shirley counted to five — there wasn't time to count to ten — then said sweetly, "I'll tell you all about it later, Mum. I really must go."

"Run along then, dear. But think about it. I expect you'll find I'm right."

Dashing into the garden and kicking the lawnmower back into life, Shirley thought about it.

It had been Alan's redundancy which had started all this, and she hadn't brought that on herself . . . had she?

She couldn't remember seeing any headlines in the local press, declaring — SHIRLEY LAMB, ETERNAL OPTIMIST AND MOTHER OF TWO, BRINGS DOWN LOCAL ENGINEERING FIRM.

Then, of course, had come the move south.

"It's a brilliant job offer," Alan had said. "We can't afford to turn it down."

Shirley had happily agreed. No-one could blame her for that.

Admittedly, it had been she who had chosen this house — mainly for its untamed jungle of a garden — but how could she have known then about Mr Grimshaw?

No-one had warned her — just as no-one and nothing had warned her about the problems they were going to have with Ben.

It had been a series of unfortunate but unavoidable circumstances, complicated by Lucy's allergies and Percy's late development, which had brought her to this moment.

It wasn't her fault at all!

Shirley wiped a bead of perspiration from her nose. There was nothing more uncomfortable than sweating on a cold, winter day.

The mower was heavy and extremely noisy and she'd been heaving it around all afternoon — playing for time, of course — determined to find a lasting solution to the problem before Mr Grimshaw's head appeared above the wall to complain again.

Goodness knows what the rest of the street thought about her mowing the grass in December.

"Your next-door neighbour's a troublemaker," Jenny, from two doors down, had told Shirley over a welcoming coffee a few days after their arrival in the new house.

"He's a serious noise freak. Name any noise and I can guarantee old Grimshaw will object to it. And not politely either!

"Then when he's finished yelling at you over the garden wall, he'll complain to the Council.

"Poor old Celia was a nervous wreck by the time she left that house."

Shirley gulped as Jenny went on, "Celia had three teenage boys, so you can imagine what it was like — music, motorbikes and Mr Grimshaw — not a happy combination."

"I suppose not." Shirley shrugged. "But we won't have that problem. Ben's seven and Lucy's only five". Jenny didn't look convinced. "You've got a car, haven't you?" she asked quite airily.

"Of course, but . . ."

"Hedge-trimmer?"

"Yes," Shirley replied, mystified.

"Lawnmower? Strimmer? I bet Alan's even got an electric drill?" she queried, raising her eyebrows.

Shirley nodded.

Jenny shook her head and pursed her lips. "Well, don't say you haven't been warned!"

A ND Shirley never did, though she often mentioned, in a lighthearted manner, that the warning had come at least a month too late.

The new house, semi-detached and showing signs of stress from its previous unruly occupants, demanded urgent attention.

The garden, an endless wilderness of briars and deep-rooted ferns, demanded even more.

Shirley tried to reason with her irate neighbour, Mr Grimshaw, assuring him that the hammering would stop, eventually; that they'd only hired the cement mixer for a week; that the children were excited and would soon calm down.

Mr Grimshaw, however, refused to be placated.

Each time his face appeared above the wall it grew a little redder.

"In my day —" His voice boomed out with predictable regularity, "— people showed their neighbours a bit of consideration. In my day, a man could hear himself think once in a while."

Alan was forced to content himself with christening the geriatric lawnmower "Grimshaw" and berating it soundly every time he had to kick it into life.

"We must maintain a policy of appeasement, Alan," Shirley encouraged. "I suppose I could bake him a cake," she suggested.

"What a brilliant idea." Alan's tone was scathing. "Make it one of your sponges. That should keep him quiet for a while."

Shirley cuffed him playfully. "The simple solutions are usually the best," she persisted. "He's an old man living on his own. He's bound to appreciate a bit of home baking. And, anyway, it'll be the thought that counts. Once he realises we're not the enemy, he'll become more tolerant, just you wait and see."

They were still waiting the day that Ben — boisterous, bouncing, but always so biddable — took to his bed and refused to go to school.

"I don't understand it," Shirley confided worriedly to Jenny. "Lucy's the shy one. Ben's so full of confidence. It never occurred to me he'd have trouble adjusting to a new school."

She drew a deep breath. "I'll have a word with his teacher. She'll get things sorted out."

Miss Hancock reported no progress two weeks later. "Ben seemed such a gregarious little lad when he first came here. But the other children must have knocked him back, dented his confidence a bit. And now he's so withdrawn I really don't know what the answer is."

Alan did.

"We'll have to move," he said. "New school for Ben, new neighbour for us — both problems solved."

"No," Shirley said. "There's got to be another way."

"Perhaps you could bake all his schoolmates a cake. I've heard boiled fruit cake goes down well, as long as your name's not Grimshaw and the currants don't get stuck behind your top plate."

Shirley continued to think. "A diversion," she said at last. "That's what Ben needs."

"A diversion?" Alan looked puzzled. "You mean we start taking him the long way round to school?"

"What I mean is . . . something to replace the children at school as the centre of his attention.

"At the moment, he can think of nothing else, right? And the more he worries about the problem, the worse the problem gets — so the more he worries about it again. It's a vicious circle. We've got to break that circle with a diversion!"

Shirley's eyes suddenly lit up. "I've thought of the perfect solution!

"We'll get him a pet!"

★★★★

"OK, Mum," Shirley mumbled to herself as she mowed. "I admit that the chicken was my idea — but for a start, it was supposed to be a hen. We wanted something not too big, or too small, or too noisy. That's what Alan said. Well, it couldn't be a dog or a cat, could it, because of Lucy's allergies? And chickens only cluck a bit, don't they!

"Ben chose it himself because it was white and because it was the boldest of the bunch.

"No-one warned us that, at that age, you couldn't always tell what sex they were. "No pun intended, Mum, but you could have knocked me down with a feather the day she started crowing. And by then it was too late!"

THEY all thought she was mad, of course, especially her mother. But what else was she to do?

Ben had been first, intrigued, then totally bewitched by little Polly.

Beneath the shelter of her ever-broadening wings his chirpiness and chatter had returned.

Polly was aggressive, greedy, demanding and completely fearless — all admirable qualities, it seemed, in the eyes of a seven-year-old boy.

"Brill!" he'd yelled victoriously, the day his new pet came of age. "I knew he couldn't be a girl."

The bedtime perch in the spare room had proved not to be the answer. It was true that bricks and mortar muffled Polly, renamed Percy's, dawn chorus far better than the garden shed, but the spare room was next to Lucy's, and Lucy screamed with rage each dawn.

Added to which was another strange and hitherto unknown phenomenon — cockerels crowed all day!

"Well, I never knew that," Alan had said with fatalistic gloom. "I always thought they only crowed at dawn. Thank goodness Mr Grimshaw's out of earshot."

Mr Grimshaw had been on sick leave in Bournemouth.

No-one knew exactly what the problem was, only that it involved his digestive system and, hopefully, had not resulted from a surfeit of boiled fruit cake.

At any rate, it was his sister, Olive, who had volunteered as ministering angel — just for a couple of weeks.

"And that's it, Mum! That's why I'm mowing the lawn. Mr Grimshaw came back yesterday evening. Last night, Percy slept in the spare room, and this morning Lucy screamed. If Mr Grimshaw hears the crowing, he'll scream, too — loud enough for the whole Town Hall to hear. Then Percy will have to go, and Ben will be back to square one.

"The lawnmower? Well . . . you see . . . it drowns out the noise of the crowing. Mr Grimshaw doesn't complain much about the hedge-trimmer and the lawnmower any more — I'm sure it's because of the fruit cake — so, this morning, I mowed the lawn.

"Of course, I know I can't keep mowing every day at this time of year, Mum. But I won't need to. There's a simple solution to this little problem.

"When I find it, I'll let you know . . ."

SHIRLEY turned instinctively, suddenly aware that she was being watched.

"I know what you're up to, Mrs Lamb," Mr Grimshaw boomed, head and shoulders strained above the wall. "But you're wasting your time. It isn't going to work."

Shirley, with an air of resignation, turned the lawnmower off.

"Now, look here, Mr Grimshaw . . ." It was a speech she'd practised many times in preparation for this moment. "Percy's here to stay."

"Percy?" Mr Grimshaw exploded. "D'you mean to tell me you've given the wretched thing a name?"

"Of course." Now she'd forgotten her lines. "It may be an unpleasant noise . . . I mean it isn't an unpleasant noise . . . not really. You'll get used to it . . ."

"Never! And I don't have to, either. There are laws to protect people like me from noises like that."

Shirley's heart sank. Now, what was the next bit? Schools — that was it! Railway lines and schools.

"If you lived next door to a school, you'd get used to the noise of the trains . . ." Her voice tailed away.

That didn't sound right somehow — and there was something else, a sort of rustling sound, distracting her attention . . .

It was Percy, strutting out on to the lawn, throwing back his head, stretching out his neck . . .

And the children were here, too.

"Mum, this is Mark!" Ben yelled as he charged up the drive.

Mr Grimshaw put a finger in his ear.

"His Mum'll collect him in an hour!" That was Jenny, shouting from the gate.

Mr Grimshaw put a finger in his other ear.

"It isn't fair! I wanted Angela to come and play," Lucy complained.

"Mark's come to see Percy," Ben pointed out.

"Percy's stupid," Lucy told him.

"You're the stupid one," Ben retorted.

Cock-a-doodle-do-oo-oo-oo.

That, of course, was Percy, determined not to be outdone.

The silence afterwards was awesome.

Ben's stemmed from pride, Mark's from admiration, Lucy's from a fit of pique and Shirley's from a sudden feeling of despair.

Mr Grimshaw, however, had removed his fingers from his ears and was staring speechlessly at Percy. His silence seemed to stem from . . . shock perhaps?

"Well, I'll be . . ." The old man shook his head. "A Light Sussex if I'm not mistaken."

"Er . . . yes." Shirley tried to sound informed. "Look, Mr Grimshaw, I'm sorry if the crowing upsets you . . ."

"Oh, but it doesn't, Mrs Lamb."

" It's just that Ben's been so unhappy . . . and . . . it doesn't?"

"In my younger days, all the folk round here kept livestock," he informed her.

"They did?"

"This is smallholding land, you see, Mrs Lamb. You can keep anything you like on it. And don't you let any interfering busybody tell you anything different!"

Shirley hadn't yet recovered from the shock. "N-n-no. I won't," she stammered.

Mr Grimshaw's face, in repose, looked almost human.

"What you can't do though, Mrs Lamb —" The fury-lines were back "— is subject a poor old man to this constant barrage of mechanical mayhem."

He wagged an angry finger in the direction of the mower. "What you can't do is call your lawnmower Percy and push it around all bloomin' afternoon in an attempt to drive me to an early grave!"

Shirley opened her mouth to protest.

Mr Grimshaw waved a hand to silence her. "I know, I know. I'm getting the picture now, Percy's the cockerel. The mower's called Fred, I presume."

"Actually, it's Grrr . . . aham." She gave a nervous little laugh.

Mr Grimshaw raised his eyes to Heaven.

"I'm sorry . . ." Shirley spread out her hands in a gesture of helplessness. "But it hasn't been easy. The garden's so overgrown.

"And we've got used to all these labour-saving gadgets. It's hard to imagine life without them . . ."

Mr Grimshaw looked surprised. "I should have thought a lady of your unusual talents could imagine anything she wanted to," he said.

"And, on the subject of fruit cakes . . . I'll be in tomorrow morning, if you were thinking of bringing one round."

Shirley smiled. "I was indeed, Mr Grimshaw," she said.

"I'm glad to hear it, Mrs Lamb," he replied.

When he'd gone, Shirley put away the mower, then stood on the closely-cropped lawn, thinking very hard.

She couldn't help feeling that her mother had been right. She'd brought it all upon herself.

But there wasn't time to crow about it now.

Lucy wasn't looking very happy — and Percy wouldn't be able to eat the jungle on his own when it started growing in the spring again.

Her eyes suddenly lit up.

"Lucy," she said to the solemn little girl at her side. "I know you feel left out, love. But I've thought of the perfect solution.

"We'll have to ask Daddy, of course, and I expect he'll groan a little bit, but what would you say to a goat . . .?" ■

A True Romantic

by Rita Williamson

That was me, all right — but I couldn't recognise real love, even when it hit me!

'M a romantic and I don't mind who knows it. There's something about moonlight, red roses and Valentines that just make me melt. I've been smitten with romance for as long as I can remember. Not for me the tree-climbing and other harum-scarum activities of the pig-tailed tomboys who were my chums and schoolfriends.

I was the sort of little girl who played with dolls, dressed up in my mum's old frocks, played "witches and fairies" and dreamed constantly of the day a Prince would drive by, realise I was his long lost love, and whisk me away to be his Princess.

Even though I did grow older and a little wiser, I never quite grew out of my love of "romance". I graduated from fairy tales to love stories and thence to inch-thick sagas of mind-boggling passion.

Even those who scorn such blatant escapism and laugh at the soft-hearted amongst us who weep at sad films or love stories didn't dampen my conviction that there's a place for romance in this fast-moving world.

In fact, I'd go so far as to say there's an abundance of it, for it must be noted that Trisha, the girl in the flat downstairs, rarely goes short of swains. There is a never-ending army of young men eager to awaken her with a kiss.

But I regret to say nothing as remotely romantic as that ever happens to me.

Well, I guess you've got the picture and so won't be too surprised that the first time romance did rather timidly tap at my window, I rushed right out and invited it in.

I also locked the doors, phoned my mother and called in the caterers.

My friend Stuart told me I was rushing things. Stuart and I grew up together, went to school together and still look out for each other.

He is somewhat wiser about the unpredictable ways of the world and guides me round its potholes. He also knows about men (being one himself) and told me firmly that I was rushing my fences.

He was right: I scared my first love clean away and drove another off the scene almost as quickly.

Stuart explained all this to me in words of one syllable until it finally sunk in. Stuart is a good friend. I don't know how I'd have got through the heartbreak over Robert without his shoulder to cry on.

Actually, Stuart's idea of a shoulder to cry on is to frown at you and say, "There, there. Now pull yourself together!" But it was better than nothing. It was all the comfort I had when Robert left me and I thought my world was over.

★★★★

Ah . . . Robert . . . I'll never forget the day Robert walked into my life. It was a beautiful autumn day and I was at peace with the world as I strolled along the footpaths that skirted the town.

I met Robert at the high stile near the church and instead of simply waiting for me to cross, he stepped forward to help me over and even steadied me as I stepped down.

In that one moment, he stole my heart. As we looked out over the fields, he pointed to a shower of yellow-gold leaves and, cool as you like, quoted a line or two of poetry.

This was my sort of guy: sensitive, poetic, handsome . . .

It took me weeks to contrive to meet him again. Then I waited agonisingly for him to suggest a date. He did and my life changed.

I was in heaven. I had a boyfriend. A tall, handsome man who was all mine. A man who loved me and knew a thousand ways of saying it.

He bought me flowers, we sipped champagne. He was a man who valued me as a woman, a man who loved me, admired me, cherished me . . .

Robert had a wonderful repertoire of romantic sweet-talk and I was more than taken in by his silver tongue.

OF course it came to a nasty end. Robert was a romantic, that's for sure. Morning, noon and night he was always ready to wine-and-dine, to kiss-and-cuddle, to whisper sweet nothings.

And, if I happened not to be around, that apparently didn't hold him back. Oh, I'm sure he loved us all in his own sweet, philandering way. But it wasn't the sort of love I wanted.

I must confess that our last row together was rather touching. He pulled out all the stops with some real tear-jerking excuses and convinced me he truly regretted two-timing me, or rather, three-timing me.

Of course, I forgave him. After all, I'm just a big softy at heart. How can you not forgive a man who kisses you just before he leaves and says: "I love you too much, Karen, to stay around and hurt you . . ." And so Robert turned and walked out of my life.

I forgave him, but I tortured myself. For two weeks I became a miserable hermit, locked in my flat in a cocoon of self-pity.

Stuart said I was seven kinds of a fool. Deep down I knew he was right, but I was in no mood to listen.

My world was over, all my love had been wasted. Listening to Stuart tell me that I was better off on my own was not the sort of truth I wanted to hear.

That was when I temporarily lost my faith in love and romance.

I decided to go shopping to cheer myself up. A new jacket and boots failed miserably in helping me to forget. Then I wandered, unthinkingly, into the next shop which happened to be a second-hand record shop.

As I browsed, distractedly, I came across an old album that I remembered Robert saying he liked. I bought it, took it home and listened to it that evening.

After a few plays I realised I knew most of the words already. I'd heard them all before, many times.

What a phoney!

Robert's whispered words of magic, that had held me enthralled, weren't even his own!

I don't know what made me feel worse, the fact that he was a cheap fraud copying lines from old songs, or the fact that I'd fallen for them.

I hurled the poor, unfortunate album across the room in disgust and it broke in as many pieces as my heart. Or so I told Stuart when he rang me some time later.

He said I was a bigger fool than he'd ever imagined.

"Actions speak louder than words, Karen," he said gruffly. "You remember that!" I nodded down the phone at him. Then he suggested a drive in the country would be better for me than sitting at home moping.

I didn't agree, but Stuart is rather persuasive and, by the end of the following day, I could almost laugh about the whole Robert episode.

Almost . . . Except I missed him . . .

ONE day I woke up and realised the misery was over. I actually felt cheerful, ready to enjoy life again.

They say time heals, and it seemed I was over the worst.

Every now and then a little cloud flitted on to my landscape as I realised that my love-life was still rather barren. But then I would recall my narrow escape and feel better.

I was explaining my thoughts one day to Stuart. He was lying on his back in the kitchen, half of him under the draining board as he wrestled with the defective plumbing that had caused a blocked sink and nasty smell in my small flat.

I gave a self-satisfied sigh. "You know, I think I'm ready for some romance again, Stuart. For a while I was put right off and almost believed that Mr Right was a figment of my mother's imagination. But I'm ready again now.

"I'm not sure where to start, though. Where can I find a nice, romantic man; someone who believes in red roses and boxes of chocolates?" I said.

Stuart sighed exasperatedly from under the sink. "Why are you so obsessed with romance?"

"Because romance is everything!"

"You talk a lot about 'romance', Karen, but what about 'love'? Isn't that more important?" Stuart's question came in an echoey sort of voice from behind the U-bend.

"Romance is love!" I said quickly, shocked at this bizarre notion. "Huh! Some men just don't understand what romance means to us women.

"Look at you, you're a nice bloke, you could have dozens of girls chasing you, but you're about as romantic as . . . as a fish finger!" I spluttered.

The hammering under the sink had stopped. "And instead of being out on the town with a gorgeous girl, you're unblocking a sink. Doesn't that tell you something?"

"Yes." The single word was uttered very quietly and I had to lean down to hear him. There was a scuffling from under the sink as Stuart wriggled out and then, suddenly, he was standing in front of me, shoving a wet rag and a wrench into my hands.

"Do you think I come round here and do this because I like it?" He looked strange, and sounded, well — angry.

"There's more to it than fascination for mucky jobs, Karen, and if you can't see it, then . . . then you're stupid!"

With that, he slammed out of the flat, leaving me to stare at my dripping tap and blocked-up sink.

What had got into him? I gazed at the greasy, lumpy water in the sink and shuddered. Goodness, what a mess and dear, sweet Stuart hadn't uttered one word of complaint.

"Now there's love . . ." The words froze on my lips as I finally realised how silly I'd been.

All these years I'd been looking for love in the wrong places. I'd thought that love was the same thing as romance; that apple blossom and white lace were just "love" in disguise. But love is nothing to do with that at all — no wonder I'd been getting it wrong.

I recalled Stuart's earlier, gruff statement about actions speaking louder than words and suddenly realised what he meant.

Love is a big hunk of a fella traipsing uncomplainingly along behind me while I visit a doll museum.

Love is a guy in jeans and a baseball cap walking my mother's poodle, collecting manure for my roses, eating my rock cakes and unblocking my sink.

Romance is letting the whole world know about it.

That evening, I invented my own definition of romance.

Romance was a dim-witted woman coming to her senses and knocking on Stuart's door with a bunch of red roses in one hand and a four-pack of beer in the other.

Stuart opened the door and stared warily at me.

"Fancy a beer?" I said and thrust the four-pack at him. He still stared at me.

"These are for you, too," I offered the flowers, hopefully, with a blush. He took them with surprise.

"Red roses?" The pleasure in his voice could not be denied.

I nodded. "For true love," I said unwaveringly, and he opened the door wide and invited me in. ■

Small Surprises...

by Sheila Ireland

Life is full of them — but this one would change their world completely . . .

THAT morning, Jennifer Wade tried to concentrate solely on the gentle hum of the lift taking her to the 11th floor of the Phoenix Beauty Corporation.

She knew that she had to try to keep her mind clear and not bring her personal problems into the office.

There was work to do, and she was already late.

Jennifer stepped out into the hallway opposite the glass doors with JENNIFER WADE: MARKETING MANAGER prominently displayed on them in bold, white letters.

The doors were electronically operated and they slid open as she approached. Then she was in the blue-carpeted foyer and her secretary was smiling at her.

"Good morning!" Sally greeted her. "So what did the doc say?"

Jennifer forced a smile, a little shrug.

"It was nothing, Sally. Doctor Preston thinks I might have overdone things at Christmas, that's all. Suggested I take a little break . . ."

It was the first time that she had lied to her secretary, she thought. But the "taking a break" part was true. More than true."Anyway, you look great, as always," her secretary called as Jennifer went through to her own office.

It was a spacious office with large picture windows overlooking the city. The thick carpeting was pale grey and on the walls there were framed photographs of the company's beauty products.

Jennifer put down her briefcase and sank into the leather chair behind her desk.

She still couldn't believe what was happening to her.

Her husband's photograph was in a silver frame on the desk. It was a recent one and she noticed that the laughter lines around his eyes were getting deeper.

"Oh, Richard," she said softly.

They had been married for more than twenty years and still loved each other deeply.

They had a good life together; settled, safe, secure. A fulfilling life, with good, solid friends.

All of that would change now, she thought.

Jack Preston was one of their friends; a gynaecologist.

She had gone to see him thinking that he was the best person to advise her.

She had just turned forty-two years of age. Things were happening to her. She'd had no doubt that it was the menopause. It was the only likely explanation.

Jack Preston had come up with another.

"Jennifer, you're pregnant," Jack had said. "I'd say you're already well into your second, possibly third month."

He had smiled at her expression.

"Richard will be excited. Break it to him gently."

Jennifer could only shake her head.

"It's impossible," she'd whispered.

Jack had come round his desk and put his hand gently on her shoulder. "Call it a miracle, Jennifer."

Jennifer checked through her appointments diary.

There was a general end-of-month meeting in the boardroom at three . . . All of the company directors would be at that meeting. It would be the proper time to tell them. The proper thing to do, if she intended going through with this pregnancy.

It just hadn't sunk in yet. She was still reluctant to admit that it was true, even to herself.

A baby, after all these years . . .

Richard should be the first to know, she thought. He would be phoning her soon from America, to let her know what time he'd be arriving back in London.

She could tell him then; drop the bombshell. Tell him that she was about to turn their lives upside down.

She noticed her hands were trembling.

She leaned back in her chair, trying to keep her emotions in check. Her office door opened and her secretary entered, bringing her a cup of coffee.

On her way out, Sally paused and said. "Are you feeling all right, Jennifer? You seem . . ."

"I'm fine, Sally." Jennifer laughed a little raggedly. "Just trying to get myself organised, that's all."

Sally nodded. "Anyway, it's Friday. The weekend's almost here."

Jennifer had forgotten the weekend.

Richard would be home tonight, anticipating nothing more than their Saturday round of golf, the club dance in the evening, the usual get-together with friends at Sunday lunchtime . . .

Jennifer drank her coffee slowly. Long ago, she had accepted that she would never be a mother.

She had buried the disappointment, the awful hurt, deep within herself, so that it no longer caused her to lie awake at night.

She and Richard had made a good life, without children.

FOR the first time, Jennifer realised that she was afraid. When the phone rang, she jumped, startled out of herself.

"Richard?"

"Hello, love. A quick call, just to let you know that I'll be home about nine.Things have gone well over here."

Jennifer could hear the pleasure and excitement in his voice. She forced herself to join in.

"That's great, Richard, but I knew you'd do well. You're an exceptional man, you know."

"Enough of this flattery. Look, love, what do you say to a bit of a celebration tonight? Just the two of us — maybe a meal out at Maxime's . . .?" Jennifer froze.

She knew she couldn't tell him. Not yet. And not at a celebration at Maxime's.

"Richard, would you mind very much if we don't — if we just stayed at home?"

"Jennifer . . ."

He was disappointed. She knew it, but there was nothing she could do.

"Jennifer, are you all right? Is there —?"

"No, Richard, nothing's wrong. I'm just a bit tired today."

"OK, love. I understand. It's been a long week. Look, I'll see you tonight. Anyway, we've got the whole weekend, haven't we?"

Jennifer put down the phone and stared blankly ahead of her.

She and Richard were used to being spontaneous. Used to arranging things at a moment's notice...

Oh, dear heaven, she thought. But she was given no time to brood.

Sally buzzed to advise her of the first of her appointments. Then two grey-suited men from the advertising agency ambled into her office, smiling and talking with bright, morning-fresh enthusiasm about the TV ads for the new foundation cream.

Jennifer returned their smiles. She shook their hands. And she forced herself to concentrate.

After that, Jack Schaeffer, the works' manager, arrived with the production schedules tucked in a folder underneath his arm.

Big, gruff and gristled, Jack was one of the company's old-timers and never wasted words. The meeting didn't last long. In the end, he nodded, satisfied.

"Proper planning, that's what counts," he said as he went out.

And Jennifer stared at him and nodded dumbly.

A planned family is a happy family.

The pain of remembering was sharp. In those early days when they were first married, it had all seemed so simple.

She and Richard had agreed there was no need to rush into having babies. They had been so blithe and so certain.

"First we need a proper home, Richard. A little white bungalow with a big back garden for them to play safely in . . ."

"Them?"

"A boy for you and a girl for me!" She'd laughed, delighted at the thought. "But later, when we're ready, all right?"

"Whatever you say, love."

Jennifer blinked. Her secretary was standing in the doorway of her office.

"I'm just popping down to the canteen, Jennifer. Can I get you anything?"

Jennifer shook her head. "No — no, thanks, Sally. I have to check through my projected budget figures before the meeting in the boardroom. I — I'm fine."

"Sure?" Sally looked concerned.

"Sure," Jennifer said steadily.

When the door closed, Jennifer sorted through the files in her desk and brought out the one marked "Finance". She opened it and began to read and check the proposed budget figures.

After a few minutes, the figures swam before her eyes and she sighed, pressed her fingers to her eyes, and remembered.

Four years after they were married, she and Richard had finally bought that little white bungalow, with the big back garden.

They had two cars in the garage and a healthy bank account and so many plans. And it was only then that they had started to worry.

Somehow she couldn't fall pregnant.

"Don't worry," Richard had told her, "there's nothing wrong . . ."

And there wasn't. Not with Richard. But the doctors had found a blockage in her Fallopian tubes and she'd thought they had found the answer.

The operation was successful, but still she couldn't become pregnant.

Jennifer sighed deeply now and shook her head. Stop it, she told herself. She looked at her watch and it was already two o'clock. She forced herself to concentre on the figures before her.

At ten to three, she sat back and rested her hands on her stomach. And it was then she remembered the baby bootees . . .

It had been over two years after her operation and it had been the worst of times. The time of despair, she thought.

She had felt it deep and cold in the very heart of her. There would be no babies.

Yet some incredible hope had still existed. And that day she'd seen the fluffy white baby bootees in the shop window and had felt that they might be some kind of good luck charm. A talisman for someone who still desperately wanted to believe in miracles.

She had bought the bootees and foolishly slept with them under her pillow. Night after night, hoping, praying.

In the end, however, there were no miracles.

JENNIFER, it's three o'clock!" Sally was in the doorway. Jennifer nodded and stood up, closing the file in front of her.

In the boardroom she said nothing about her pregnancy, although it was becoming more and more real to her.

She was aware of her baby resting under her heart, palpable and real.

She was remembering what Dr Jack Preston had told her.

"At your age, there are dangers in childbirth, both for you and the baby, Jennifer. You'll have to start slowing down, taking things easier. Maybe even give up your job . . ."

She was relieved when the chairman declared the meeting closed and very glad when the day finally ended and she found herself back in the lift, going down.

THEY still lived in the little white bungalow with the big back garden. Jennifer busied herself in the kitchen. She had prepared the lamb casserole with herbs and seasonings, ready for the oven.

It was seven-thirty. About now she would usually have treated herself to a martini. Tonight, she resisted.

She finished in the kitchen and went through to the lounge.

The radio was playing; Perry Como crooning about the good times. And she let the sadness wash over her as she sat down.

She had finally buried the longing to have a baby. It was then the tears had stopped, she remembered.

Richard had been so good, so patient, so understanding about it all, and, in the end, it was he who'd helped her to accept that it was over.

"It doesn't matter, Jennifer," he had said quietly one night. "Stop torturing yourself. We've got each other. That's all I've ever wanted."

She hadn't believed him. Until, through her tears, she had seen the seriousness of his face — and heard the grimness in his voice.

"I'm telling you the truth, Jennifer." He had cupped his hands around her face. "I love you. You're all that's ever mattered. I don't want children. I've never wanted children . . ."

Now, Jennifer sat on the couch, chilled, as if by a breeze.

She stared dispassionately around the room, not quite knowing where to look, but seeing a home designed solely for adults. A beautiful home with no place for nappies or toys . . .

She stood up slowly and walked out of the room.

★★★★

The ladder to the attic pulled down smoothly, easily. Jennifer climbed the steps in a daze. She didn't know why she was doing this, she told herself.

It was dark there and it took her a moment to find the light switch. Then the dusty place was bathed in yellow light and she could see the big trunk in the corner.

She crossed the floor, knelt in front of it, then paused, uncertain now whether to continue with this. Yet it seemed unavoidable, almost inevitable, like the movement of a tide.

She lifted the lid of the trunk, reached inside and found the little tissue paper package in the corner, under the dishevelled bric-a-brac, the discarded things of long ago.

The fluffy white baby bootees, protected by their packaging, were as they had always been. Soft and beautiful and miraculous.

Jennifer held them to her face, feeling their baby softness. She had never been able to bring herself to throw them away.

For the first time since she'd heard the news, she cried.

★★★★

It was there that Richard found her when he got home. She was still holding the baby bootees and her face was stained with tears.

"Oh, Jenny, Jenny," he said gently, lifting her from her knees into his arms. "Whatever's wrong?"

He sounded so concerned, so loving.

Jennifer blinked back a fresh flow of tears.

"Richard, I'm sorry. I can't explain what's happened, but —"

She swallowed hard. "I'm pregnant."

Richard look stunned. He frowned in the pale-yellow dusty light and his arms tightened around her.

He led her downstairs and took her in his arms again as, by now, she was sobbing uncontrollably. It was a while before she could speak.

"You never wanted children, Richard. I never meant for this to happen . . ." The rest of the sentence was muffled as she turned her face into the warmth of his sweater.

Gently, he pushed her away from him and made her look into his eyes.

"A long time ago," he said softly, "I saw my wife cry herself to sleep at nights and tear herself apart because she couldn't have children.

"It hurt very badly and I thought there was nothing I could do. Until one day, Jennifer, I decided to tell a little white lie . . ."

Jennifer stared at him.

"I told a lie, Jennifer," Richard said again, with a smile. Her smile grew with his till they were both laughing.

★★★★

Six months, one week and four days later in a small, private maternity ward, Anne Louise Wade was born — five pounds, four ounces and in perfect health.

The mother cried as she held the baby in her arms.

The father cried, too.

He was holding his son, Richard Jnr., born just minutes before his little sister. ■

A poem by Joyce Stranger, inspired by
an illustration by Mark Viney.

THE MIRACLE

A walk in the woods
Knee deep in snow.
Wild deer are leaping
Into sunset's red glow.
My small son beside me
Holds tight to my hand.
It's Christmas tomorrow
But it's not what I
planned.
My company's bankrupt
No wages they'll pay.
We'll have very short
commons
On this Christmas Day.

But my small son is
leaping
Up and down in delight.
Church bells are pealing
And sound on the night.
Sleigh bells are ringing.
Voices are singing.
Santa is coming.
My young son is
running.
Robin and rabbits
Red squirrel and deer.
All the beasts of the
forest
Seem gathered here.

The reindeer are
prancing,
My little son's dancing.
"Santa, come calling.
Please don't forget."

Time to go home.
It's cold and too late
For my youngster to
roam.
I turn into our street
With slow dragging feet.

The dark house is bright
With colour and light.
Friends wait to greet us.
My wife runs to meet us.
Santa's called with
presents galore
Bringing comfort and
happiness
Right to our door.

I look out of the window.
There in the sky,
I see a sledge shining
As it passes by.
As long as I live
I will never forget
How Santa turned
sorrow to joy
For the best
Christmas yet.

149

"Jenny's Back"

by Isobel Stewart

Those two words struck fear into my heart. Strange to think she'd once been my best friend . . .

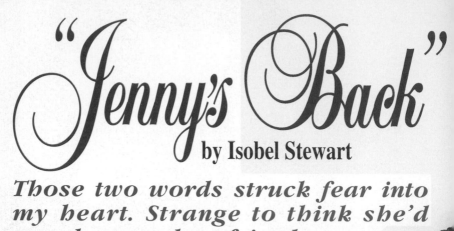

IF you don't go away, you can't come back. Yes, but if you don't go away, you don't have to come back.

Jenny and I read that somewhere, years ago.

Would it be better, we wondered at the time, to stay here, in the small seaside town we loved, or would we appreciate it more by going away and coming home?

I was sure that I would be the one to go, and Jenny the one to stay.

Jenny was the quiet one. Small and dark, she used to follow where I led.

When we were small, she would stand at the edge of the group of children, happier just to watch, joining in only when I took her hand and drew her in.

Later, when we were older, and there were parties, dramatic societies, debating societies and the Church Youth Club to attend, she would join in only because I wanted to and because we were friends.

I was restless then, eager to see the world. And she would listen to all my hopes and dreams.

Sometimes, afterwards, I wondered if I really would have wanted to go away, if it hadn't been so clear that David had chosen Jenny.

David was part of our group, although he was a year or two older. His father owned a big hardware store, and David joined him as soon as he left school.

By the time Jenny and I left school, it was obvious that David and Jenny were a pair.

"Are you sure you don't mind, Lynn?" Jenny said a little uncertainly, when she told me that she and David were going to the church picnic together.

"Mind?" I said — and even now I remember how lightly I said it. "Why should I mind? I'm probably going with Paul — unless I decide to go with Dennis."

Jenny's brown eyes were concerned.

"Goodness, Jenny," I said, airily, "I like David, but you know me — I'm not the faithful kind. I believe in safety in numbers. Anyway, David's so right for you. He's actually a bit too quite for me, a bit, well, unadventurous, maybe."

Jenny smiled. "That suits me," she said, softly. "Since I'm much the same."

And she was. Quiet, shy, happy with her job at the bank, content with the tiny diamond ring David gave her a year later and the plans they were making for a wedding the following summer.

My own plans to go away had to be put on hold, because my mother had been ill. But it wouldn't be long, I remember telling Jenny confidently, before I would be free to leave.

"You'll come back for the wedding, Lynn?" Jenny asked me.

"Of course," I said. And by then, I think I really believed that it didn't matter to me that David and Jenny would be married next summer.

But before their wedding date was even set, the film crew came to Seahaven. I can't remember what film they were making. There was no-one well-known in it, but it was exciting for all of us.

He was a cameraman, the American Jenny fell in love with.

It all happened with such bewildering swiftness, that I can hardly remember what he looked like. Sun-bleached hair, blue, blue eyes . . . laughing eyes, someone said, after they had gone.

Small, quiet Jenny, in the space of a few weeks, fell in love with this stranger, told David she couldn't marry him, stood up to her parents, and went away to marry her cameraman and live in America.

We didn't say goodbye. My mother had to see specialists, and I went with her. When we came back, it was all over. Jenny was gone, and David was alone.

Not long after, David and I met outside the bank where Jenny had worked.

"How's your mother, Lynn?" David asked.

"Much better," I told him. And then, because it had to be said — "Oh, David, how could she?"

The shattered look on his face stopped me going any further.

"I don't want to talk about it, Lynn," he said steadily.

And so we didn't.

Not even when we began going out together, nor when David asked me to marry him, more than two years later.

I had one letter from Jenny, a few weeks after she went away. She said, quite simply, that she was sorry she hadn't been able to see me, sorry she had hurt David, and she hoped I would understand.

She gave me her name — Mrs Elliott Parker — and her address and she said she hoped that I'd write to her.

I didn't write. And after I had read her letter, I tore it up.

About a year later, her father died, and her mother left Seahaven. By then, David and I were seeing each other regularly.

Jenny was gone from our lives, but I would catch myself at odd moments unaccountably remembering and wondering about how David felt.

Oh, I tried to speak to him about it. I didn't want Jenny's memory to cast a shadow over our marriage. But every time I started to ask about her, something made me stop. I suppose I was scared what his answer would be.

I WAS waiting outside the school for Robbie to come out, when I heard. This was his first year at "big" school, and although he insisted he could come home by himself, I liked to be there to meet him.

I was thinking that I would stop after this term, when I realised Mary Harris was speaking to me.

"Sorry, Mary," I said, "what were you saying?"

"I said, I suppose you've seen Jenny?" she repeated.

"She's back," one of the other mothers said, a little awkwardly.

"No," I said carefully, "No, I haven't seen her. Is he — is her husband here, too?"

"No, she's on her own," Mary said. "Staying at the hotel."

The school bell rang then and the children came out.

We went home, and there was just time to heat up the soup I'd made earlier, and put out some rolls, before David arrived.

I could think of nothing but the knowledge that Jenny had come back.

At last, when Robbie had gone out to play with the dog, I told David.

"Jenny's back!" I said, more abruptly than I'd meant to.

"Jenny?" he said, startled. "Jenny Martin?"

"Jenny Parker," I corrected him.

"Have you seen her?" he asked.

I shook my head, and told him that I'd only just heard.

"I wonder what brought her back?" David said. "After all these years!"

It was 15 years since she had gone away. I knew that, without thinking about it. I wondered if he did, too.

★★★★

Next day I went to see her. Mrs Parker had gone out, the receptionist at the hotel told me. I didn't know whether to feel relieved or disappointed.

Outside, I hesitated. I could turn left and do some shopping on the way home, or I could turn right and walk along to the harbour.

I went to the harbour and Jenny was there, as I had half expected her to be. She was walking with her hands thrust deep in the pockets of her thick cardigan, her dark head bent. She didn't see me at first.

We had always looked for pansy shells together. I wondered, foolishly, if she was still looking.

It wasn't until she climbed up the steps from the sand that she saw me.

"Lynn?" she said. And then, not quite steadily, "Oh, Lynn."

"Hello, Jenny," I said, carefully. "I heard you were back."

We looked at each other.

Once, long ago, there had been no need for words between us, we had been so close.

Now, we both had problems finding enough to bridge the gap between us.

"I heard that you and David got married," Jenny said.

"Yes," I answered. "Yes, we've been married for twelve years."

It was a long time after you left him, I thought, before he turned to me.

"We have three children," I said then, a little too quickly. "Tessa's ten, Karen's eight, and Robbie's just six. And you?"

"We had no children," she said, very quietly.

Had? She obviously saw the question in my eyes.

"Elliott died three years ago. A car crash, while he was filming."

"I'm sorry, Jenny," I said, all too conscious of how inadequate the words were.

"I'm getting used to being on my own now. It was pretty awful at first. In some ways, because we had no children, we needed each other even more. But they were good years, and I've reached the stage now where I'm just grateful for what we had."

We turned and walked back towards the town together, talking quietly.

"Are you here for long?" I asked her.

"Only a week. I have to get back. I've sold my house, you see, and there's so much cleaning out to do before I move."

She hesitated, then added a little awkwardly, "I would like to meet your children, Lynn. And to see David. Would that — could I do that?"

"Of course," I said brightly — too brightly. "We'd love that. How about coming for dinner tomorrow night?"

D O you mind, love?" I said, when I told David that Jenny was coming to visit us.

He was busy putting new hinges on one of the kitchen cupboards, and didn't look round.

"Mind? Of course not. It'll be great to see Jenny again."

All those years ago, he had said he didn't want to talk about what she had done to him. But that had been a long time ago.

Now all I had to say was, "How do you really feel about her coming back?" It wouldn't be unnatural to ask, yet somehow my lips couldn't form the words.

I wondered all day long, as I made a chicken pie and a trifle, collected Robbie from school and sorted out a quarrel between Tessa and Karen, what they would say to each other when they met.

But, of course, with the children there, there wasn't even a moment of awkwardness.

The girls were a little shy at first, but soon they were taking Jenny upstairs to see their room and their toys.

She came with me to say goodnight to Robbie and, as we were going back through the hall, she said, "He's very like David, isn't he? They must be such a joy to you, your children."

I couldn't begin to think what a life without our children would be. But something kept me from being able to say that to Jenny who had no children. Jenny, who was the same age as I was, and who was a widow.

It was a harsh, bleak word, I had sometimes thought, and I found it shocked me to apply it to someone with whom I had once been so close.

When she had gone, David took out some accounts he had to work on for the shop. I cleared up, and as I went in and out from the kitchen, I looked at him, his dark head bent over his work.

Again I wanted to ask him how he had felt, seeing Jenny again, but couldn't. I would have sensed any regrets and I wouldn't have been able to bear it.

I told myself firmly that David loved me. I knew we had a happy marriage and there could never be any possibility of anything coming between us.

But after all, I was second best. The thought shook me. Did I still believe that?

Well, part of me reasoned, it was Jenny David had chosen, Jenny he would've married, if she hadn't met her American and gone away with him.

But I couldn't let myself dwell on that now. In a few days Jenny would go away, out of our lives once again. Everything would return to normal and it would be as if Jenny had never come back.

Or so I told myself.

I MET Jenny in the High Street the next day, and she asked me if we would join her for a pub lunch at the hotel on Sunday, the day before she was to leave.

Sunday duly arrived.

When the children had finished eating, they went to play on a swing in the garden — the girls taking turns to push Robbie. Then David had to push — first Tessa, and then Karen.

Jenny and I watched from our table at the window.

"I don't know who's enjoying that more," Jenny said, smiling.

David came back to join us. When the coffee arrived, he asked Jenny, easily, naturally, if she had found it very different, living in California.

"Well, yes. It was a bit of a culture shock at first."

She went on to tell us about the people, and the different places they had lived.

Quite casually, she mentioned the names of some of the people she had met through her husband's work, names I had seen only on screens or in newspapers.

She wanted to hear all our gossip, too, and by the time we'd filled in the gaps, it was time to go.

That night, after the children were in bed, we sat reading the Sunday papers. I noticed, very soon, that David was just sitting, the newspaper in his hands.

At last, heart thumping, I asked, "What are you thinking about, David?"

"I'm thinking about Jenny," he said slowly.

My heart lurched.

He put the newspaper down and came over to sit beside me on the couch, and took both my hands in his.

"I keep thinking about her being alone, with no children, no living memory of her Elliott. It's sobering, Lynn." His hands tightened on mine. "It makes me realise how lucky we are."

He held me close to him, and there was no need for words. I knew that everything was all right between us — always had been. There were no regrets.

I HADN'T intended to see Jenny again, but the next morning, after the children left for school, I walked along to the hotel.

Her face lit up when she opened the door.

"Lynn, I'm so pleased to see you," she said. "I've finished packing, but I don't leave till twelve."

We walked along the harbour wall, and then on to the beach.

"That first day — were you looking for pansy shells?" I asked her.

For a moment she looked surprised, and then she smiled.

"No," she said. "I think I was just remembering."

"Remembering?" I asked, carefully.

"Elliott and I were walking on the beach here, the day I knew that I loved him," Jenny said, her voice low. "I — I think, in a way, I was finally letting go, saying my last goodbye to him."

She stopped.

"When I go back home," she said, "I'm going to marry a man I've known for a long time. He was a friend of Elliott's. His wife died years ago. I've known his children all their lives, and they'll accept me. But I had to come back here, first.

"Do you remember, Lynn," she said, "how we used to wonder about staying here, and not having to come back, or going away and being able to come back?"

"I remember," I said, a little unsteadily.

And suddenly, the distance between us was gone, the distance of the years, and of what had happened.

I can't remember all that we said, but I do remember this.

"I've seen the way David looks at you, Lynn. You're his life, his world, you and the children. That's how it was with Elliott and me, too.

"It will be different with Hugh, but, I hope we will become like that in time. You are very lucky, Lynn."

It was a moment before I could answer.

"I know that," I said, and I did.

We reached the hotel, and said goodbye.

I left her, then, and walked home. It was beginning to rain and there was the smell of the sea on the wind.

All I loved in the world was here, and I was happy that I had been the one to stay, the one who had no need to come back, because I'd never left.

Perhaps, I thought, as I strolled through the dear familiarity of my home town, perhaps, all those years ago, I had been second best for David. But perhaps not.

Perhaps before he asked me to marry him I had already become first in his heart. As I knew I was now.

We should talk about it. We never had, but it wasn't too late.

The rain was heavier now, but it didn't matter, because I was home. ■

"My Lucky Mascot"

by
Nicola
Slade

It was strange, but as soon as her lodger moved in, Fortune began to shine on her.

THE cat was there again. "Look, I'm sorry, Cat," Jane sighed. "It's no use looking at me like that, there's no way you're moving in with us. I can't afford to feed the two of us, let alone a pet."

The cat sat stolidly on the dustbin.

"I can't take you in," Jane wailed in guilty irritation.

The cat had been sitting on her dustbin every day for the last week when she came in from picking up Alexander from the child-minder. It didn't miaow at her, or rub itself ingratiatingly round her legs, or purr in proper pussycat fashion. It just sat and stared at her.

Today, as she popped Alexander in his lobster-pot playpen while she filled the kettle, she looked out of the small basement window.

The cat seemed to sense her gaze and swivelled its head round, making it look like a skinny owl. The yellow eyes glared at her and she knew what it wanted.

"Cats don't use much vocal communication amongst themselves," she read somewhere, "they use body language instead." The cat outside was conducting a body language conversation with her, and she was having to force herself to ignore it.

Maybe it was somebody's much-loved pet, specialising in emotional blackmail as a hobby. Maybe it would go home when it got bored.

She made scrambled eggs for herself and Alexander, cutting the toast into fingers for him to chew on.

Slowly she spooned the baby's egg into the little mouth which was opening and shutting like a robot starling chick.

She read him a story, then they played for a while, enjoying the warmth and closeness of a cuddle until it was time to bath him.

Jane enjoyed Alexander's bath-time even more than her son. She gloried in the baby's happy chuckles, gurgles and splashes.

"I don't know, Alexander," she informed him as she towelled him dry, fluffing up his absurd topknot of dark down. "They all said we'd never manage, but we do, don't we?"

Alexander agreed with a bounce and a beaming smile, tactfully ignoring the wobble in his mother's voice as she made her brave declaration.

She gave him his last bottle and, after a final hug and kiss, laid him down in the cot beside her own bed in the alcove of the tiny rented basement flat.

There was nothing on television worth watching and she'd managed to catch up with her marking and preparation for her job as an English teacher at lunchtime.

So now she would enjoy the rare luxury of doing nothing, absolutely nothing at all.

"Stupid!" she scolded herself, five minutes later, as she fussed around the flat tidying and dusting and even scouring the kitchen sink.

It was no use, she couldn't settle to an idle evening, no matter how tired she felt; there was always this sense of having to keep going, never being able to relax her guard. Then the phone rang.

"Hello, Mother." Jane held the receiver at arm's length and frowned, preparing to listen in resigned silence as her mother launched into her usual diatribe of Jane's inadequacies and her father's thoughts on the subject.

"So I told that Mrs Fisher, 'Jane's doing very well,' I said."

"What?" Jane could hardly believe her ears. Her mother had actually said something nice about her? Had praised her to someone, instead of brushing her under the carpet as an object of shame?

Was there a little extra warmth in her voice when she asked about her only grandchild?

Jane put the phone down gently, feeling a warm, friendly glow suddenly towards the whole of mankind.

If Mum was coming round, then perhaps Dad would, too. It had been hard on them, Jane knew only too well, having their only daughter fall madly, irresponsibly in love with a married man in her last year at teacher training college.

When she'd told Don of her pregnancy he hadn't wanted to know. Though her parents had been shocked, they'd stood by her, never questioning her decision to go ahead with having the baby. They had been there for her in every way, in every practical way, and Jane was eternally grateful, but oh how she longed sometimes for a return to the old footing of their relationship.

She wanted to be Jane, their precious only child, their miraculous late achievement, their pride and joy, their glittering prize.

Jane managed, during the daytime, to put on a brave face, to cope, but at home, alone, when Alexander was asleep, she sometimes felt her heart would break with the loneliness.

And now, maybe, just maybe, it looked as though her parents were coming round, and maybe, just maybe, she and Alexander would be able to go home for some time in the Easter holiday that was looming.

Her warm glow of happiness made her want to embrace the whole world and when she glanced out of the window she saw it was raining.

In the murky gloom of a cold, wet evening she saw a movement on the dustbin in the tiny back yard.

The cat was still there.

"Oh, all right!" She flung open the door and confronted the persistent feline.

"'I can't cope with any more responsibility, but if you promise to behave yourself and not get too attached, I suppose you can come in."

She had actually succeeded in surprising the cat. It sat upright in the rain and stared at her, eyes narrowed, looking for the catch.

OK, no catch.

It stretched, shook itself and leapt nimbly down from the dustbin, watching her all the time as it strolled nonchalantly across the yard and up to the door. On the doorstep, it paused and looked at her again, took her measure and decided Jane was on the level.

The cat came in. Jane shut the door, gently but firmly, not wanting to frighten the animal with too sudden a movement, but being tough and streetwise, it ignored her.

Jane grabbed an old towel and rubbed the sopping wet fur, feeling the thinness of the animal under the ragged coat. It was hungry. She could tell, though the cat still disdained the usual cat ploys to seduce her into feeding it; sitting there on her lap in scruffy dignity. But she knew what it wanted.

Body language again.

"I'll have a look in the cupboard and see what there is," she told the cat, depositing it on the sofa.

"How do you feel about baked beans?" she enquired, rummaging in her small store of food, absurdly cheered by the advent of this ragged interloper. "Or spaghetti?

"No, hang on, here's something. Where on earth did I get this tin of pilchards, I wonder?"

The tin of pilchards had a raffle ticket stuck on with sticky tape, prize relic of a First Year charity tombola last term. The cat rapidly disposed of the half tin she put down for it.

It ate ravenously but daintily, keeping an eye on Jane as she made ready for bed, stretching the cat-net someone had given her over Alexander's cot, then it condescended to accept the folded towel in a cardboard grocery box that was on offer.

"Goodnight, Cat," she murmured sleepily, turning out the light. She felt a tremulous optimism tonight, what with Mum's call and now the cat's company . . .

A rustle and fidget was all she got in reply as the cat stirred and resettled itself, but just as she was drifting into sleep, she felt a hesitant warmth on her feet and a tentative purring.

NEXT morning Jane woke to the sound of Alexander gurgling cheerfully. He had pulled himself up in his cot, and he and the cat were communing happily.

She realised, surprised, that she had slept right through the night. Feeling really rested for once, she lay there dreamily watching the two of them make friends — Alexander, from behind the bars of his cot, the cat from his position on the bed.

Then Alexander squealed in delight as she hauled him out of his cot for a quick cuddle before they launched themselves on the day.

"It's no use pretending to be so tough!" she laughed at the cat. "I saw the way you looked at Alex; you're an old softy underneath!" And she tickled the affronted cat under the chin.

By the time she got to school, Jane was conscious of an unfamiliar itching on her back which she tried to ignore. Only tension, she told herself. But by lunchtime she had admitted to herself that it was more than a stress rash.

"What if it's fleas!" she gasped aloud.

"Huh?" She hadn't noticed that Mike Bramley, deputy head of the biology department, had sat down beside her on the park bench.

The grapevine said that his girlfriend of several years had gone off with another man a couple of months ago. Jane had felt sorry for him but had schooled herself to remain aloof from staff-room gossip.

She had only enough energy to divide between work and Alexander, there wasn't room for anyone else. Today, however, it was Friday, the sun was shining, her parents seemed to be coming round and she had a cat for company, so today she could cope with other people.

"I said I think I've got fleas!" she repeated and when he stared at her in disbelief, she explained about the cat.

"Well, I've got some flea powder at home," he volunteered. "I could drop it round to you this evening? The sooner you do something about it, the better."

She was touched at his concern.

"That's very kind of you, Mike," she replied gratefully. "I didn't know you had a cat?"

A shadow fell across his nice, friendly face. "Maybe not for much longer," he said mournfully.

"Humphrey's at the vet's today, having an operation. Some maniac got him in a hit-and-run accident last night, and it's touch and go."

Jane was warmly sympathetic and they chatted amicably on their way back to school.

AFTER Alexander was tucked up in his cot, she had a quick tidy round. Then as eight o'clock passed, she began to wonder if Mike had had second thoughts . . .

"Well, Cat," she mused, "at least I've got you for company." The cat purred softly.

There was a gentle knocking at the door and there was Mike, staggering under a large cardboard box, a bunch of flowers poking out from under his arm, and two plastic carrier bags wafting a warm, oriental smell before him.

"Hi!" he puffed, divesting himself of his various burdens. "This looks like an awful imposition and you can tell me to go away if you like, but I wondered if you'd join me in a Chinese takeaway? This is it, here."

"That's really nice of you, Mike," she said delightedly, taking the bag. "What a lovely idea. Sure you don't mind dining with someone who's flea infested?" Mike shook his head and smiled.

As she hastily warmed plates under the grill and laid the tiny table, Mike put a bottle of wine down beside the Chinese meal.

"How's Humphrey?" Jane asked. For a moment there was no reply and when she looked up, Mike was looking sad.

"He didn't make it," he said simply. "That's why I hoped you wouldn't mind me coming round. I just felt like some company. I've brought round Humphrey's tins of cat food," he explained. "They're no use to me now, so I thought perhaps you could use them."

The cat sat, sphinx-like, surveying the scene while they ate, sizing up this new human.

About half-past nine the phone rang. It was Jane's mother again, sounding oddly uncertain.

"We were wondering, dear . . ." she began diffidently ". . . or at least, Daddy said it would be nice, if . . . if perhaps we could some up and see you on Sunday?"

"That . . . that would be lovely, Mum," she gulped. "But look, why don't you both come here to lunch? OK . . . fine . . . see you then . . ."

Her eyes were shining with unshed tears as she put the phone down and smiled at Mike. Suddenly life beckoned instead of threatened; she had turned the corner, she and Alexander.

Jane wondered if Mike would like to come to lunch on Sunday too; maybe she'd ask him tomorrow. He'd already suggested a joint shopping trip when he discovered she had no car.

★★★★

The cat didn't bother to pretend it was sleeping in the cardboard box tonight, and jumped up with her as soon as she tucked herself under the duvet.

It settled at her feet contentledy.

Jane yawned and curled up in a warm, happy ball. For the first time in what seemed like forever, she had a weekend to look forward to, a family visit, a friend . . .

"Thanks, Cat," she murmured sleepily. We'll have to think of a name for you tomorrow, won't we?"

★★★★

She slept, and the cat pondered. It hoped it would end up with a sensible name, but, on balance, it didn't really care.

Just like Jane, the cat had a warm, glowing, forward-looking feeling, and just like Jane, outwardly so tough, so capable, so self-sufficient, it was so desperately in need of love and affection. It stretched languidly then curled up, dreaming dreams. ∎

New, Life New Hope

by Dorothy L. Garrard

She loved him for himself, but also for the memories he held . . .

THE baby fell asleep over his bottle, his mouth pursed like a wet, pink rosebud. Anna gently wiped away the dribbles of milk and stood up, holding him against her shoulder, until he burped gently. Then she laid him in the pram and wheeled him on to the lawn, covered him lightly against the summer breeze and left him to his dreams.

Indoors, she looked round, wondering what to do first, though she could scarcely be bothered with any of it. But next week she would start her job-share with Barbara. Each of them would be taking turns looking after the babies, so it made sense to get her house in order while she had the chance.

She was lucky that Barbara had given birth at about the same time, and their mutual boss had been so accommodating.

Lucky? She picked up Ray's photograph from the sideboard, touching the glass between them, hard and cold as the weight where her heart used to be.

Only 14 months of marriage — and he hadn't even seen his son. Killed on an icy January road, hurrying from work to the hospital where she'd been taken in premature labour.

They had brought her his flowers and the gift-wrapped book of poems found in the car.

She had unwrapped the book and leafed through it, numbly. Her eyes took in a couple of lines, and once she would have thought — how beautiful. But at that moment they had mocked her with their unreality and her own foolish romanticism.

"When I'm in hospital," she had said to him only a few days before, "bring me a poetry book to read; poems about flowers and trees."

"And birds and bees?" Ray had grinned, kissing her. Though they had laughed together, Anna hadn't given up the fanciful notion that if her mind was full of lovely, tranquil things, the baby would absorb the beauty, too.

Even then, reading the verse, she hadn't been able to cry. She'd felt she'd been transported into a different kind of existence where there was no purpose to anything.

Smiling emptily, she'd gone through the motions, so that people would imagine all was well and leave her alone.

Everyone said how very like her the baby was. Were they inferring that it would have been harder, if he reminded her of Ray? And would it? She had no idea . . .

NOW she switched on the radio and whisked around with such attention to detail that it was lunchtime before she knew it. And the baby was still asleep!

She made herself a snack, appreciating this unexpected break, for he seemed prone to small Infections, which made him fretful and demanding.

Looking out of the window, Anna saw the pram blanket move, and went out to check on her son.

In the spring, a blackbird had taken up residence in the pear tree, waking her in the early hours with its sweet, piercing song. It was still fluting persistently and this time it had probably disturbed the baby.

He was fully awake, eyes of a deep, clear blue, like her own, fixed on the pear tree with the intense wide-eyed excitement of a kitten.

He was normally a solemn baby, perhaps sensing her own lack of joy. But as the breeze fluttered the leaves, his legs pumped on the mattress, his fists waved, and seeing his mother, he smiled.

Anna's legs went weak.

The smile was totally Ray's, wide, impish and familiar, brimming with the joy of the moment. For an instant, Ray was there, at one with them and the summer day.

Her grief released at last, tears welled up and blinded her.

She picked up her son but the baby kept his face turned to the tree, crowing at the breeze-blown leaves.

Those two persistent lines of poetry flashed into her head again, as clearly as if Ray himself had spoken them. *"If I keep a green bough in my heart, the singing bird will come."*

The warmth of the joy of life flowed through the birdsong, and the child, into Anna; the endless cycle of renewal. She pressed her lips to the baby's downy head and smiled through the healing tears.

"Yes," she said softly, against his cheek, "you are definitely your father's son. Let me tell you about him . . ." ∎

All The Things We Are

by Teresa Ashby

Our past had moulded us, made us who we were. So would it be wise to throw it all away?

"A RE you sure?" Jack asked, as Sue held Lotus Blossom for the last time. She looked at him, blinking back silly tears. She knew they were silly, because far worse things had happened to her than parting with a cuddly toy!

"Of course I'm sure," she said resolutely, and shoved Lotus Blossom into the box with a dozen other assorted cuddly toys.

"We said everything, didn't we? Anyway, you're giving up Bert!"

Bert was already in the boot, tucked between a magazine rack and a stack of assorted paperbacks.

The boot was stuffed, the back seat piled to the roof, and Sue had another box on her lap as Jack drove them to the car boot sale.

It was early as they swung into the grounds of Sedgeleigh House, yet the place was busy.

The traders, the professional car-booters and the plain enthusiastic were there already, their stalls groaning beneath the weight of their goods.

Jack and Sue grabbed their pitch, parked, and weren't even out of the car before two dozen people descended on them.

Even as Jack opened the boot, hands were flying in, grabbing things.

And the onslaught didn't abate until another car arrived.

"Phew!" Jack breathed at last, as the bargain hunters piled across towards the newcomers. "How much did you take?"

She held out her hand. "About twenty pounds," she said. "What happened?"

"I don't know." He shook his head. "But I have the awful feeling that we've been done!"

They'd planned for ages how to handle this. Priced everything up in their minds, but all that had gone to pot in the confusion of that first rush.

They set up the rest of the stuff — what little remained of it — on and around the decorating table.

Sue deliberately set Lotus Blossom at the back, trying to hide her behind a pile of old magazines.

Jack did the same with Bert, pushing him under the table, behind a box of assorted mismatched crockery.

Everything, they'd agreed – all the old reminders of the past. A fresh start meant just that. They had to clear the old flotsam and jetsam from their lives.

A woman came over and picked up Lotus Blossom, casting what looked like a professional eye over her. "Her ears are missing," she said. "How much?"

"Two pounds," Sue said, even though she'd mentally priced her already at just twenty pence.

"Phaw!" the would-be Lotus Blossom-buyer snorted, and tossed Lotus Blossom back.

Lotus Blossom was a large, cuddly toy that Mike, her ex-husband, had bought for her on their first wedding anniversary.

She'd been beautiful then, all silky, ivory-coloured fur and a gorgeous expression. She'd come with a huge blue satin bow around her neck.

Mike had hugged Sue, crushing Lotus Blossom between them. She'd loved him so much then, so very, very much.

The love they'd shared on their wedding day seemed to grow and intensify as the years passed, especially when the children were born and they'd wept tears of joy together.

They'd been so happy then. It was like a fairy-tale romance and Sue thought they would live happily ever after.

But real life got in the way, of course.

Lotus Blossom fell prey to grubby little hands that pulled and tugged, and mouths that chewed and sucked.

The end of her tail was bitten off, her ears disappeared and she quickly became the worse for wear.

She used to sit on the bed in all her silky beauty but, as the cracks began to appear in their marriage, so her appearance altered.

It was almost as if her condition mirrored the state of Sue's life — the sorry, tatty fur a mirror of a sorry, tatty marriage.

She could remember, with almost painfully clarity, lying on the bed, cuddling Lotus Blossom, her tears soaking into her fur after Mike had gone.

He'd met someone else, someone who rang bells, he said, someone with whom he'd fallen in love.

It was suddenly as if all the years in between no longer mattered.

All the happiness, crises, good times and bad they'd gone through together, counted for nothing.

It hurt because Sue had still loved him as much as ever and she'd been blind to the gradual breakdown.

So Mike had gone off to start his new life with his new love, leaving Sue and the children behind to rebuild theirs.

JACK watched Sue bristle every time anyone showed an interest in Lotus Blossom.

She wanted to get rid of the toy because Mike had bought it for her, yet she seemed reluctant to part with it now.

He could never see why she was so fond of the tatty old thing anyway. Although . . . He looked down at Bert.

Peg had bought Bert for Jack when they'd been still at school.

They had done everything together in those days — studied, played — they even did their paper rounds as a pair.

Bert was Jack's lucky mascot and, on his little tank top, the words Male Chauvinist Pig had been embroidered. Not that the message was legible now.

It had been meant as a joke, but Peg had always been a bit of a feminist.

Bert was actually a sort of chimp — or maybe a bear. Jack never could decide what kind of animal he was meant to be.

Bert had sat on the invigilator's desk while Jack sat his exams. Jack was sure it was down to him that he'd obtained such good grades.

He'd gone along on Jack's driving test, too, and Jack had passed first time. It had been the same with job interviews and that time he'd had to see the bank manager about a loan . . .

And, of course, Bert had been given pride of place in their first two-roomed home.

He was getting a bit scuffed round the edges by then and a churn in the washing machine at the laundrette had sort of rearranged his interiors, so he looked a bit odd.

Then a mouse got him. It chewed his bottom and pinched some of his stuffing and, although Peg had stitched him up (needlework wasn't her strong point), he never looked the same.

But Jack still loved him, even though the note she'd left for him had been propped up against Bert.

By then, they'd been living in a fashionable semi on a new estate.

Their lives had changed since those early days of togetherness in two rooms — changed beyond recognition. And so had they.

He supposed they'd simply grown up — and grown apart.

She'd just gone. There wasn't anyone else, she'd said in her cruel little note, but she couldn't stand living with Jack any more.

The truth was, that although she was fond of him, he got on her nerves and she just had to get away.

She'd done it in style, too. She'd gone on a trip round the world in a mini-bus with a crowd of travel-mad students — and had never come back.

A MAN came over just then and chuckled as he picked Bert up. "He looks well-loved," he said. "What are you asking?"

"Five pounds," Jack said out of the corner of his mouth so that Sue wouldn't hear. They'd agreed to let him go for twenty pence, the same as Lotus Blossom.

"You don't really want to part with him, do you?" The man chuckled a bit more and wagged his finger at Jack.

Jack knew, of course, that he had to let Bert go eventually.

Anything they didn't sell would invariably end up either at a jumble sale or on the rubbish tip — and Jack couldn't bear to see Bert in a bin.

Jack was miles away, Sue realised. A man had nearly bought Bert from him, then he'd seemed to change his mind.

Not that Sue blamed Jack. Bert was a tatty old thing and a constant reminder of Jack's life with Peg.

She really didn't want any reminders like that in their new home and could understand why Jack wanted to get rid of him.

But she couldn't help being a little fond of Bert herself.

Hadn't he been there, sitting in the back seat of the car on the night that Jack proposed?

"Now it's quiet, why don't you have a stroll round?" Jack's voice broke into her thoughts. "You might be able to pick up a bargain."

"Mmm," Sue said. "There's a plant stall down there. I could pick up a few plants for our new garden."

The new house was ready and waiting for them. The garden was completely laid to grass and they'd already planned to dig out some flower beds.

With a last fond look at Lotus Blossom, Sue wandered off, walking slowly past the other stalls, deep in thought.

Mike and Sue had never had much of a garden. She was the keen gardener and so, when it came to choosing a house, they'd somehow ended up with one with a tiny square at the back.

That summed up their lives together quite nicely. What Sue wanted went by the board, because what Mike wanted always had to come first.

Until he'd left her, Sue hadn't even known she had a mind of her own.

Or perhaps it happened when she met Jack.

They had so much in common but, if they did disagree, Jack never belittled her, or made her feel silly for feeling differently.

If she'd ever dared to contradict or disagree with Mike, he'd been furious. He'd always had to be right, all the way down the line.

Eventually, she'd been afraid to think for herself for fear of being ridiculed.

He'd left her with their marriage in tatters and her confidence shattered.

Then Jack had come along, picked up the pieces and put her back together again.

SHE bought a selection of perennials and some herbs and returned to the car, to find Jack selling five wine glasses for 50 pence.

"It got busy just after you left," he said. "Oh, you got some plants. Good. I'll stick them in the boot. We don't want to sell them by mistake, do we?"

He grinned and her heart flipped over. She loved Jack so much.

He'd been so good for her.

And, while it was never the same as it had been with Mike, it was somehow better, deeper, more precious.

"There's a chap over there selling good gardening tools," Sue told him. "You said you wanted to get some."

"Mind if I take a look?"

"Go ahead," she smiled. "You can pick us up coffee on your way back."

She watched him hurry off — dear Jack.

Then she looked over the stall. Lotus Blossom had gone!

Her stomach turned over as she searched frantically through the boxes that remained, her heart sinking.

Had she been taken by some grimy-faced child to be tortured and pulled apart before finally being tossed into a bin?

She deserved better than that!

Bert was still sitting there, she noticed, with his ugly little monkey/bear face. He looked rather smug.

She picked him up and glared at him. Jack said he was like a lucky mascot. Well, he hadn't brought much luck in his relationship with Peg. It was as well they'd never married.

Although she'd never met Peg, she didn't like her at all.

The woman must have been half crazy to let a guy like Jack slip through her fingers.

★★★★

The coffee was burning Jack's fingers through the plastic cups, as he hurried back to the stall.

Sue was looking extremely pleased with herself. "I've been rushed off my feet since you left! I even managed to sell that pair of ugly vases Mike's mother bought us. Five pounds the pair! Can you believe that?

"It just goes to show — one person's junk is another's treasure."

Jack put the coffee down on the edge of the pasting table and looked at the depleted stock. "We could think of going soon," he murmured. "There's not a lot left worth selling."

"Didn't you get any tools?"

"Not on your nelly! I can get them cheaper in town," he said.

Then he saw it and his heart seemed to freeze inside his chest — the empty space where Bert had sat.

He rummaged round, pretending to be checking what was left, but really he was looking frantically for Bert.

There was no trace of him.

Jack felt nauseous.

"Look, some people are packing up and leaving." Sue's voice broke into his shattered thoughts. "What do you say to calling it a day?"

His heart felt heavy as he packed what was left into the boot, before they drove away from the sale.

"Did you buy any nice car boots?" Sue's neighbour asked with a chuckle as they pulled up outside.

She laughed too, but, inside, her heart was aching.

She was going to miss Lotus Blossom terribly. Who on earth would she tell all her secrets to now?

After he'd dropped Sue off, Jack drove home with a heavy heart. Almost everything was packed in tea chests, ready for the big moving day.

There was a dusty space on the mantelpiece where Bert used to sit.

They'd been through so much together, Bert and Jack, so very much — and now he'd gone. What would he do for a lucky mascot now?

It was daft to get so sentimental over a stuffed toy, especially when he had things to do, a wedding to prepare for!

THE church was packed and Jack, standing at the front with his best man, shuffled nervously.

"Brides are always a little late," the vicar whispered, his voice warmly reassuring. "It's almost a tradition."

Sue arrived precisely two minutes late, on the arm of her 12-year-old son, who was giving her away.

They were followed by her daughters, looking like fairy princesses in their bridesmaids' outfits.

The beautiful dress Sue wore had a full skirt in oyster-coloured silk and a bodice of soft, rose-pink velvet.

Jack turned and watched as she came down the aisle towards him and felt as if the love welling inside him might overflow.

Sue looked at him, loving him, knowing in her heart that, this time, it was forever.

She'd been too young before to know what she was doing, but this time her eyes were open wide.

"I love you," he whispered, as she joined him in front of the vicar.

"I love you, too," she said confidently.

The vicar smiled benignly, his eyes moist. He knew real love when he saw it.

After the service, the photographs and the reception, they went back to their new home.

The children were staying with friends and relations for that first night, and so they had the place to themselves.

"I have something for you," Jack said. "A special gift."